BENJAMIN FRANKLIN.

MEN OF ACHIEVEMENT

INVENTORS

BY

PHILIP G. HUBERT, Jr.

FINIS·CORONAT·OPVS

NEW YORK

CHARLES SCRIBNER'S SONS

1894

TROW DIRECTORY
PRINTING AND BOOKBINDING COMPANY
NEW YORK

PREFACE

THIS book, dealing with our great inventors, their origins, hopes, aims, principles, disappointments, trials, and triumphs, their daily life and personal character, presents just enough concerning their inventions to make the story intelligible. The history is often a painful one. When poor Goodyear, the inventor of vulcanized rubber, was one day asked what he wanted to make of his boys, he is said to have replied: "Make them anything but inventors; mankind has nothing but cuffs and kicks for those who try to do it a service."

Meanwhile, the value of the work done by great inventors is widely acknowledged. In a remarkable sketch of the history of civilization, Professor Huxley remarked, in 1887, that the wonderful increase of industrial production by the application of machinery, the improvement of old technical processes and the invention of new ones, constitutes the most salient feature of the world's progress during the last fifty years. If this was true a few years ago, its truth is still more apparent to-day. It is safe to say that within fifty years power, light, and heat will cost half, perhaps one-tenth, of what they do now; and this virtually means that in 1943 mankind will be able to buy decent food, shelter, and clothing for half or one-tenth of the labor now required. Steam is said to have reduced the working hours of man in the civilized world from fourteen to ten a day. Electricity will mark the next giant step in advance.

With the many and superb tools now at our service, of which our fathers knew comparatively nothing—steam, electricity, the telegraph, telephone, phonograph, and the camera—we and our descendants ought to accomplish even greater wonders than these. As invention thus rises in the scale of importance to humanity, the history of the pioneers and, to the shame of mankind be it said, the martyrs of the art, becomes of intense interest. In the annals of hero-worship the inventor of the perfecting press ought to stand before the great general, and Elias Howe should rank before Napoleon. Whitney, Howe, Morse, and Goodyear, to mention but a few of our Americans, contributed thousands of millions of dollars to the nation's wealth and received comparatively nothing in return. Their history suggests as pertinent the inquiry whether our patent laws do not need a radical change. The burden and cost of proving that an invention deserves no protection ought to fall upon whoever infringes a patent granted by the Government. At present it is all the other way.

P. G. H., JR.

New York, September, 1893.

CONTENTS

LIST OF ILLUSTRATIONS

FULL-PAGE

ILLUSTRATIONS IN THE TEXT

INVENTORS

I.

BENJAMIN FRANKLIN.

BENJAMIN FRANKLIN'S activity and resource in the field of invention really partook of the intellectual breadth of the man of whom Turgot wrote:

> " Eripuit cœlo fulmen, sceptrumque tyrannis."

> " He snatched the thunderbolt from heaven,
>   And the sceptre from the hands of tyrants."

And of which bit of verse Franklin once dryly remarked, that as to the thunder, he left it where he found it, and that more than a million of his countrymen co-operated with him in snatching the sceptre. Those persons who knew Franklin, the inventor, only as the genius to whom we owe the lightning-rod, will be amazed at the range of his activity. For half a century his mind seems to have been on the alert concerning the why and wherefore of every phenomenon for which the explanation was not apparent. Nothing in nature failed to interest him. Had he lived in an era of patents he might have rivalled Edison in the number of his patentable devices, and had he chosen to make money from such devices, his gains would certainly have been fabulous. As a matter of fact, Franklin never applied for a patent, though frequently urged to do so, and he made no money by his inventions. One of the most popular of these, the Franklin stove, which device, after a half-century of disuse, is now again popular, he made a

The Franklin Stove.

present to his early friend, Robert Grace, an iron founder, who made a business of it. The Governor of Pennsylvania offered to give Franklin a monopoly of the sale of these stoves for a number of years. "But I declined it," writes the inventor, "from a principle which has ever weighed with me on such occasions, viz. : That as we enjoy great advantages from the inventions of others, we should be glad of an opportunity to serve others by any invention of ours; and this we should do freely and generously. An ironmonger in London, however, assuming a good deal of my pamphlet (describing the principle and working of the stove), and working it up into his own, and making some small change in the machine, which rather hurt its operation, got a patent for it there, and made, as I was told, a little fortune by it."

The complete list of inventions, devices, and improvements of which Franklin was the originator, or a leading spirit and contributor, is so long a one that a dozen pages would not suffice for it. I give here a brief summary, as compiled by Parton in his excellent " Life of Franklin." " It is incredible," Franklin once wrote, " the quantity of good that may be done in a country by a single man who will *make a business* of it and not suffer himself to be diverted from that purpose by different avocations, studies, or amusements." As a commentary upon this sentiment, here is a catalogue of the achievements of Benjamin Franklin that may fairly come under the title of inventions:

He established and inspired the Junto, the most useful and pleasant American club of which we have knowledge.

He founded the Philadelphia Library, parent of a thousand libraries, and which marked the beginning of an intellectual movement of endless good to the whole country.

He first turned to great account the engine of advertising, an indispensable element in modern business.

He published " Poor Richard," a record of homely wisdom in such shape that hundreds of thousands of readers were made better and stronger by it.

He created the post-office system of America, and was the first champion of a reformed spelling.

He invented the Franklin stove, which economized fuel, and suggested valuable improvements in ventilation and the building of chimneys.

He robbed thunder of its terrors and lightning of some of its power to destroy.

He founded the American Philosophical Society, the first organization in America of the friends of science.

He suggested the use of mineral manures, introduced the basket willow, promoted the early culture of silk, and pointed out the advisability of white clothing in hot weather.

He measured the temperature of the Gulf Stream, and discovered that northeast storms may begin in the southwest.

He pointed out the advantage of building ships in water-tight compartments, taking the hint from the Chinese, and first urged the use of oil as a means of quieting dangerous seas.

Besides these great achievements, accomplished largely as recreation from his life work as economist and statesman, Benjamin Franklin helped the whole race of inventors by a remark that has been of incalculable value and comfort to theorists and dreamers the world over. When someone spoke rather contemptuously in Franklin's presence of Montgolfier's balloon experiments, and asked of what use they were, the great American replied in words now historic: " Of what use is a new-born babe?"

" This self-taught American," said Lord Jeffrey, in the *Edinburgh Review* of July, 1806, " is the most rational, perhaps, of all philosophers. He never loses sight of common sense in any of his speculations. No individual, perhaps, ever possessed a greater understanding, or was so seldom obstructed in the use of it by indolence, enthusiasm, or authority. Dr. Franklin received no regular education; and he spent the greater part of his life in a society where there was no relish and no encouragement for literature. On an ordinary mind, these circumstances would have produced their usual effects, of repressing all sorts of intellectual ambition or activity, and perpetuating a generation of incurious mechanics; but to an understanding like Franklin's, we cannot help considering them as peculiarly propitious, and imagine that we can trace back to them distinctly almost all the peculiarities of his intellectual character."

The main outlines of Franklin's life and career are so familiar to everyone, that I may as well pass at once to the story of his work as an inventor. We all know, or ought to know, that Benjamin, the fifteenth child of Josiah Franklin, the Boston soap-boiler, was born in that town on the 17th of January, 1706, and established himself as a printer in Philadelphia in 1728. That he prospered and founded the *Gazette* a few years later, and became Postmaster of Philadelphia in 1737; that after valuable services to the Colonies as their agent in England, he was appointed United States Minister at the Court of France upon the Declaration of Independence; and that in 1782 he had the supreme satisfaction of signing at Paris the treaty of peace with England by which the independence of the Colonies was assured. That he died full of honors at Philadelphia in April, 1790, and that Congress, as a testimony of the gratitude of the Thirteen States and of their sorrow for his loss, appointed a general mourning throughout the States for a period of two months.

The great invention or discovery which entitles

Franklin's Birthplace, Boston.

Benjamin Franklin to rank at the head of American inventors was, of course, the identification of lightning with electricity, and his suggestion of metallic conductors so arranged as to render the discharge from the clouds a harmless one. In order to appreciate the originality and value of this discovery, it is necessary to review briefly what the world knew of the subject at that day.

For a hundred years before Franklin's time, electricity had been studied in Europe without much distinct progress resulting. A thousand experiments had been performed and described. Gunpowder had been exploded by the spark from a lady's finger, and children had been insulated by hanging them from the ceiling by silk cords. A tolerable machine had been devised for exciting electricity, though most experimenters still used a glass tube. Several volumes of electrical observations and experiments had appeared, and yet what had been done was little more than a repetition on a larger scale, and with better means, of the original experiment of rubbing a piece of amber on the sleeve of the philosopher's coat. Experimenters in 1745 could produce a more powerful spark and play a greater variety of tricks with it than Dr. Gilbert, the English experimenter of 1600, but that was about all the advantage they had over him.

So-called experts had attempted, with more or less satisfaction to themselves, to answer the question addressed by the mad Lear to poor Tom: "Let me talk with this philosopher. What is the cause of thunder?" Pliny thought he had explained it when he called it an earthquake in the air. Dr. Lister announced that lightning was caused by the sudden ignition of immense quantities of fine floating sulphur. Jonathan Edwards, in his diary of 1722, records the popular impression of the day upon this subject: "Lightning," he says, "seems to be an almost infinitely fine combustible matter, that floats in the air, that takes fire by sudden and mighty fermentation, that is some way promoted by the cool and moisture, and perhaps attraction of the clouds. By this sudden agitation, this fine floating matter is driven forth with a mighty force one way or other, whichever way it is directed, by the circumstances and temperature of the circumjacent air; for cold and heat, density and rarity, moisture and dryness, have almost an infinitely strong influence upon the fine particles of matter. This fluid matter thus projected, still fermenting to the same degree, divides the air as it goes, and every moment receives a new impulse by the continued fermentation; and as its motion received its direction, at first, from the different temperature of the air on different sides, so its direction is changed, according to the temperature of the air it meets with, which renders the path of the lightning so crooked."

Even this explanation was a daring bit of speculation in Jonathan Edwards, for thunder and lightning were then commonly regarded as the physical expression of God's wrath against the insects He had created.

Mr. Peter Collinson, the London agent of the library that Franklin had founded in Philadelphia in 1732, was accustomed to send over with the annual parcel of books any work or curious object that chanced to be in vogue in London at the time. In 1746 he sent one of the new electri-

Franklin Entering Philadelphia.

cal tubes with a paper of directions for using it. The tubes then commonly used were two feet and a half long, and as thick as a man could conveniently grasp. They were rubbed with a piece

2

of cloth or buckskin, and held in contact with the object to be charged. Franklin had already seen one of these tubes in Boston, and had been astonished by its properties. No sooner, therefore, was it unpacked at the Library, than he repeated the experiments he had seen in Boston, as well as those described by Collinson. The subject completely fascinated him. He gave himself up to it. Procuring other tubes, he distributed them among his friends and set them all rubbing. "I never," he writes in 1747, "was before engaged in any study that so totally engrossed my attention and my time as this has done; for what with making experiments when I can be alone, and repeating to my friends and acquaintances, who, from the novelty of the thing, come continually in crowds to see them, I have during some months past had little leisure for anything else."

Franklin claimed no credit for what he achieved in electricity. During the winter of 1746–7 he and his friends experimented frequently, and observed electrical attraction and repulsion with care. That electricity was not created, but only collected by friction, was one of their first conjectures, the correctness of which they soon demonstrated by a number of experiments. Before having heard of the Leyden jar coated with tin-foil, these Philadelphia experimenters substituted granulated lead for the water employed by Professor Maschenbroeck. They fired spirits and lighted candles with the electric spark. They performed rare tricks with a spider made of burnt cork. Philip Syng mounted one of the tubes upon a crank and employed a cannon-ball as a prime conductor, thus obtaining the same result without much tedious rubbing of the tube.

The summer of 1747 was devoted to preparing the province for defence. But during the following winter the Philadelphians resumed their experiments. The wondrous Leyden jar was the object of Franklin's constant observation. His method of work is well shown in his own account of an experiment during this winter. The jar used was Maschenbroeck's original device of a bottle of water with a wire running through the cork.

" Purposing," writes Franklin, " to analyse the electrified bottle, in order to find wherein its strength lay, we placed it on glass, and drew out the cork and wire, which for that purpose had been loosely put in. Then, taking the bottle in one hand, and bringing a finger of the other near its mouth, a strong spark came from the water, and the shock was as violent as if the wire had remained in it, which showed that the force did not lie in the wire. Then, to find if it resided in the water, being crowded into and condensed in it, as confined by the glass, which had been our former opinion, we electrified the bottle again, and placing it on glass, drew out the wire and cork as before ; then, taking up the bottle, we decanted all its water into an empty bottle, which likewise stood on glass ; and taking up that other bottle, we expected, if the force resided in the water, to find a shock from it. But there was none. We judged then that it must either be lost in decanting or remain in the first bottle. The latter we found to be true; for that bottle on trial gave the shock, though filled up as it stood with fresh unelectrified water from a tea-pot. To find, then, whether glass had this property merely as glass, or whether the form contributed anything to it, we took a pane of sash glass, and laying it on the hand, placed a plate of lead on its upper surface; then electrified that plate, and bringing a finger to it, there was a spark and shock. We then took two plates of lead of equal dimensions, but less than the glass by two inches every way, and electrified the glass between them, by electrifying the uppermost lead; then separated the glass from the lead, in doing which, what little fire might be in the lead was taken out, and the glass being touched in the electrified parts with a finger, afforded only very small pricking sparks, but a great number of them might be taken from different places. Then dexterously placing it again between the leaden plates, and completing a circle between the two surfaces, a violent shock ensued; which demonstrated the power to reside in glass as glass, and that the non-electrics in contact served only, like the armature of a loadstone, to unite the force of the several parts, and bring them at once to any point desired; it being the property of a non-electric, that the whole body instantly receives or gives what electrical fire is given to, or taken from, any one of its parts.

" Upon this we made what we called an electrical battery, consisting of eleven panes of large sash glass, armed with thin leaden plates, pasted on each side, placed vertically, and supported at two inches' distance on silk cords, with thick hooks of leaden wire, one from each side, standing upright, distant from each other, and convenient communications of wire and chain, from the giving side of one pane to the receiving side of the other ; that so the whole might be charged together with the same labor as one single pane."

In 1748 Franklin, being then forty-two years old, and in the enjoyment of an ample income from his business as printer and publisher, sold out to his foreman, David Hall, and was free to devote himself wholly to his beloved experiments. He had built himself a home in a retired spot on the outskirts of Philadelphia, and with an income which in our days would be equivalent to $15,000 or $20,000 a year, he was considered a fairly rich man. Having thus settled his business affairs in a manner which proved that he knew perfectly well what money was worth, he took up his electrical studies again and extended them from the machine to the part played in nature by electricity. The patience with which he observed the electrical phenomena of the heavens, the acuteness displayed by him in drawing plausible inferences from his observations, and the rapidity with which he arrived at all that we now know of thunder and lightning, still excite the astonishment of all who

read the narratives he has left us of his proceedings. During the whole winter of 1748–49 and
the summer following, he was feeling his way
to his final conclusions on the subject. Early
in 1749 he drew up a series of fifty-six observations, entitled "Observations and Suppositions
towards forming a new Hypothesis for explaining the several Phenomena of Thundergusts."
Nearly all that he afterward demonstrated on
this subject is anticipated in this truly remarkable paper, which was soon followed by the most
famous of all his electrical writings, that entitled "Opinions and Conjectures concerning
the Properties and Effects of the Electrical
Matter, and the Means of preserving Buildings,
Ships, etc., from Lightning; arising from Experiments and Observations made at Philadelphia, 1749."

Franklin sets forth in this masterly paper the
similarity of electricity and lightning, and the
property of points to draw off electricity. It is
this treatise which contains the two suggestions
that gave to the name of Franklin its first celebrity. Both suggestions are contained in one
brief passage, which follows the description of a
splendid experiment, in which a miniature lightning-rod had conducted harmlessly away the
electricity of an artificial thunder-storm.

"If these things are so," continues the philosopher, after stating the results of his experiment,
"may not the knowledge of this power of points
be of use to mankind in preserving houses,
churches, ships, etc., from the stroke of light-

ning, by directing us to fix on the highest part of those edifices upright rods of iron, made sharp as a needle and gilt to prevent rusting, and from the foot of those rods, a wire down the outside of the building into the ground, or down round one of the shrouds of a ship, and down her side till it reaches the water? Would not these pointed rods probably draw the electrical fire silently out of a cloud before it came nigh enough to strike, and thereby secure us from that most sudden and terrible mischief?"

The second of these immortal suggestions was one that immediately arrested the attention of European electricians when the paper was published. It was in these words:

"To determine the question, whether the clouds that contain lightning are electrified or not, I would propose an experiment to be tried where it may be done conveniently. On the top of some high tower or steeple, place a kind of sentry-box, big enough to contain a man and an electric stand. From the middle of the stand let an iron rod rise and pass, bending out of the door, and then upright twenty or thirty feet, pointed very sharp at the end. If the electrical stand be kept clean and dry, a man standing on it, when such clouds are passing low, might be electrified and afford sparks, the rod drawing fire to him from a cloud. If any danger to the man should be apprehended (though I think there would be none), let him stand on the floor of his box, and now and then bring near to the rod the loop of a wire that has one end fastened to the leads, he holding it by a wax handle; so the sparks, if the rod is electrified, will strike from the rod to the wire and not affect him."

A friend once asked Franklin how he came to hit upon such an idea. His reply was to quote an extract from the minutes he kept of the experiments he made. This extract, dated November 7, 1749, was as follows: "Electrical fluid agrees with lightning in these particulars: 1. Giving light. 2. Color of the light. 3. Crooked direction. 4. Swift motion. 5. Being conducted by metals. 6. Crack or noise in exploding. 7. Subsisting in water or ice. 8. Rending bodies it passes through. 9. Destroying animals. 10. Melting metals. 11. Firing inflammable substances. 12. Sulphurous smell. The electric fluid is attracted by points. We do not know whether this property is in lightning. But since they agree in all the particulars wherein we can already compare them, is it not probable they agree likewise in this? Let the experiment be made."

In this discovery, therefore, there was nothing of chance; it was a legitimate deduction from patiently accumulated facts.

It was not until the spring of 1752 that Franklin thought of making his suggested experiment with a kite. The country around Philadelphia presents no high hills, and he was not aware till later that the roof of any dwelling-house would have answered as well as the peak of Teneriffe. There were no steeples in Philadelphia at that day. The vestry of Christ Church talked about erecting a steeple, but it was not begun until 1753. On the 15th of June, 1752, Franklin decided to fly that immortal kite. Wishing to avoid the ridicule of a failure, he took no one with him except his son, who, by the way, was not the small boy shown in countless pictures of the incident, but a stalwart young man of twenty-two. The kite had been made of a large silk handkerchief, and fitted out with a piece of sharpened iron wire. Part of the string was of hemp, and the part to be held in the hand was of silk. At the end of the hempen string was tied a key, and in a convenient shed was a Leyden jar in which to collect some of the electricity from the clouds. When the first thunder-laden clouds reached the kite, there were no signs of electricity from Franklin's key, but just as he had begun to doubt the success of the experiment, he saw the fibres of the hempen string begin to rise. Approaching his hand to the key, he got an electric spark, and was then able to charge the Leyden jar and get a stronger shock. Then the happy philosopher drew in his wet kite and went home to write his modest account of one of the most notable experiments made by man.

Franklin's fame as the first to suggest the identity of lightning and electricity would have been safe, however, even without the famous kite-flying achievement. A month before that June thunderstorm his suggestions had been put into practice in Europe with complete success. Mr. Peter Collinson, to whom Franklin addressed from time to time long letters about his experiments and conjectures, had caused them to be read at the meetings of the Royal Society, of which he (Collinson) was a member. That learned body, however, did not deem them worthy of publication among its transactions, and a letter of Franklin's containing the substance of his conjectures respecting lightning was laughed at. The only news that reached Philadelphia concerning these letters was that Watson and other English experimenters did not agree with Franklin. It was only in May, 1751, that a pamphlet was finally published in London, entitled " New Experiments and Observations in Electricity, made at Philadelphia, in America." A copy having been presented to the Royal Society, Watson was requested to make an abstract of its contents, which he did, giving generous praise to the author.

Before the year came to a close Franklin was famous. There was something in the drawing down, for mere experiment, of the dread electricity of heaven that appealed not less powerfully to the imagination of the ignorant than to the understanding of the learned. And the marvel was the greater that the bold idea should have come from so remote a place as Philadelphia. By a unanimous vote the Royal Society elected Franklin a member, and the next year bestowed upon him the Copley medal. Yale College and then Harvard bestowed upon him the honorary degree of Master of Arts.

As might have been expected, there was no lack of opposition to the new doctrine of lightning-rods. Every new movement of radical character is denounced more or less fiercely. The last years of Newton's life were perplexed by the charge that his theory of gravitation tended to " materialize " religion. Insuring houses against fire was opposed as an interference with the prerogatives of deity. The establishment of the Royal Society was opposed upon the ground that the study of natural philosophy, grounded, as it was, upon experimental evidence, tended to

The Franklin Penny.

weaken the force of evidence not so founded; and this objection was deemed of sufficient weight to call for serious answer. Franklin's daring proposal to neutralize the "artillery of heaven," of course could not escape, and the impiety of lightning-rods was widely discussed, often with acrimony. Mr. Kinnersley, one of Franklin's friends, who lectured for several years upon electricity, when advertising the outline of his subject always announced his intention to show that the erection of lightning-rods was " not chargeable with presumption nor inconsistent with any of the principles either of natural or revealed religion." Quincy relates in his "History of Harvard College," that in November, 1755, a shock of earthquake having been felt in New England, a Boston clergyman preached a sermon on the subject, in which he contended that the lightning-rods, by accumulating the electricity in the earth, had caused the earthquake. Professor Winthrop, of Harvard, thought it worth while to defend Franklin. "In 1770," Mr. Quincy adds, "another Boston clergyman opposed the use of the rods on the ground that, as the lightning was one of the means of punishing the sins of mankind, and of warning them from the commission of sin, it was impious to prevent its full execution." And to this attack also Professor Winthrop replied. Apparently Franklin himself thought it wise to conciliate the opposition of some so-called religious people of the day, for an account of the lightning-rod which appears in *Poor Richard's Almanac* for 1753, written probably by Franklin, begins as follows: "It has pleased God in his Goodness to Mankind, at length to discover to them the Means of securing their Habitations and other Buildings from Mischief by Thunder and Lightning."

Franklin bore his honors with the most remarkable modesty. It was in June that he flew his first kite, but not until October that he sent to Mr. Collinson an account of the experiment, and even then he described the manner of making and flying the kite and omitted all reference to his own success with it. The identity of lightning with electricity having been established by M. Dalibard, he deemed it unnecessary to forward the account of an experiment which, however brilliant, he thought superfluous. Accordingly, we have no narrative by Franklin of the flying of the kite. We owe our knowledge of what occurred on that memorable afternoon to persons who heard Franklin tell the story. Franklin prefaces his description of his kite with these words: " As frequent mention is made in public papers from Europe of the success of the Philadelphia experiment for drawing the electric fire from clouds by means of pointed rods of iron erected on high buildings, it may be agreeable to the curious to be informed that the same experiment has succeeded in Philadelphia, though made in a different and more easy manner, which is as follows." And then we have the description of the kite, the letter ending without reference to what he himself had done with it.

Yet he was far from hiding the pleasure his fame brought him. "The *Tatler*," he wrote, in 1753, to a friend, "tells us of a girl who was observed to grow suddenly proud, and none could guess the reason, till it came to be known that she had got on a pair of new silk garters. Lest you should be puzzled to guess the cause, when you observe anything of the kind in me, I think I will not hide my new garters under my petticoats, but take the freedom to show them to you in a paragraph of our friend Collinson's last letter, viz.—But I ought to mortify, and not indulge, this vanity; I will not transcribe the paragraph—yet I cannot forbear." Then he quotes the paragraph, which mentions the honors done him by the King of France and the Royal Society.

For twenty years Franklin continued to work at electricity, devoting most of his leisure to his beloved study. The great practical value of the lightning-rod, at one time in the early part of this century somewhat exaggerated, as a perfect protection against harm by lightning, just as electricity was at one time heralded as a panacea for all bodily ailments, has of late years been questioned, but the consensus of scientific opinion still attributes much merit to the device, and the extent of Franklin's services to science in the matter cannot be called into doubt. Others have claimed his discoveries. The Abbé Nolet, of France, has been credited as being the first to note the similarity between electricity and lightning; and M. Romas, of Nerac, France, is said to have used a kite with a copper wire wound around the string, to attract electricity from clouds, some time before Franklin made his experiment. But posterity has ignored these claimants, and Franklin had the happiness of escaping bitter contentions with rivals. In fact, there could hardly have been a quarrel with a man who claimed nothing, who mentioned with honor everybody's achievements but his own, and who recorded his most brilliant observations in the plural, as though he were but one of a band of investigating Philadelphians.

Passing now to Franklin's connection with the

use of oil to still dangerous waves, I had occasion recently to note that Lieutenant W. H. Beehler, of the United States Navy, in writing upon the matter, quotes Franklin's explanation of why oil works so beneficently as the accepted theory. Franklin was greatly interested, when at sea, in studying the matter. Any phenomenon that puzzled him was fit subject for investigation. Let us see how he went about the inquiry. "In 1757," he wrote, "being at sea in a fleet of ninety-six sail bound against Louisburg, I observed the wakes of two of the ships to be remarkably smooth, while all the others were ruffled by the wind which blew fresh. Being puzzled with the differing appearance, I at last pointed it out to our captain and asked him the meaning of it. 'The cooks,' says he, 'have, I suppose, been just emptying their greasy water through the scuppers, which has greased the sides of those ships a little;' and this answer he gave me with an air of some little contempt, as to a person ignorant of what everybody else knew. In my own mind I at first slighted his solution, though I was not able to think of another; but recollecting what I had formerly read in Pliny, I resolved to make some experiment of the effect of oil on water, when I should have opportunity. Afterwards, being again at sea in 1762, I first observed the wonderful quietness of oil on agitated water, in the swinging glass lamp I made to hang up in the cabin, as described in my printed papers. This I was continually looking at and considering, as an appearance to me inexplicable. An old sea captain, then a passenger with me, thought little of it, supposing it an effect of the same kind with that of oil put on water to smooth it, which he said was a practice of the Bermudians when they would strike fish, which they could not see if the surface of the water was ruffled by the wind. The same gentleman told me he had heard it was a practice with the fishermen of Lisbon, when about to return into the river (if they saw before them too great a surf upon the bar, which they apprehended might fill their boats in passing) to empty a bottle or two of oil into the sea, which would suppress the breakers, and allow them to pass safely. A confirmation of this I have not since had an opportunity of obtaining ; but discoursing of it with another person, who had often been in the Mediterranean, I was informed that the divers there, who, when under water in their business, need light, which the curling of the surface interrupts by the refractions of so many little waves, let a small quantity of oil now and then out of their mouths, which rising to the surface smooths it, and permits the light to come down to them. All these informations I at times resolved in my mind, and wondered to find no mention of them in our books of experimental philosophy.

" At length being at Clapham where there is, on the common, a large pond, which I observed one day to be very rough with the wind, I fetched out a cruet of oil and dropped a little of it on the water. I saw it spread itself with surprising swiftness upon the surface ; but the effect of smoothing the waves was not produced ; for I had applied it first on the leeward side of the pond, where the waves were largest, and the wind drove my oil back upon the shore. I then went to the windward side, where they began to form ; and there the oil, though not more than a teaspoonful, produced an instant calm over a space several yards square, which spread amazingly, and extended itself gradually, till it reached the lee side, making all that quarter of the pond, perhaps half an acre, as smooth as a looking glass.

"A gentleman from Rhode Island told me it had been remarked that the harbor of Newport was ever smooth while any whaling vessels were in it; which probably arose from hence, that the blubber, which they sometimes bring loose in the hold, or the leakage of their barrels, might afford some oil to mix with that water, which, from time to time, they pump out to keep their vessel free, and that some oil might spread over the surface of the water in the harbor and prevent the forming of any waves."

Thus Franklin collected his facts, taking them far and near, and from anybody and everybody. By dint of observation and reflection he finally solved the problem, arriving at the conclusion that " the wind blowing over water thus covered with a film of oil, cannot easily catch upon it, so as to raise the first wrinkles, but slides over it, and leaves it smooth as it finds it."

Another remarkable instance of Franklin's pas-

3

sion for investigation is afforded in the following interesting letter to Sir John Pringle: "When we were travelling together in Holland, you remarked that the canal boat in one of the stages went slower than usual, and inquired of the boatman what might be the reason; who answered that it had been a dry season, and the water in the canal was low. On being asked if it was so low that the boat touched the muddy bottom, he said no, not so low as that, but so low as to make it harder for the horse to draw the boat. We neither of us at first could conceive that, if there was water enough for the boat to swim clear of the bottom, its being deeper would make any difference. But as the man affirmed it seriously as a thing well known among them, and as the punctuality required in their stages was likely to make such difference, if any there were, more readily observed by them than by other watermen who did not pass so regularly and constantly backwards and forwards in the same track, I began to apprehend there might be something in it, and attempted to account for it from this consideration, that the boat in proceeding along the canal must, in every boat's length of her course, move out of her way a body of water equal in bulk to the room her bottom took up in the water; that the water so moved must pass on each side of her, and under her bottom, to get behind her; that if the passage under her bottom was straitened by the shallows, more of the water must pass by her sides, and with a swifter motion, which would retard her, as moving the contrary way ; or that, the water becoming lower behind the boat than before, she was pressed back by the weight of its difference in hight, and her motion retarded by having that weight constantly to overcome. But, as it is often lost time to attempt accounting for uncertain facts, I determined to make an experiment of this, when I should have convenient time and opportunity.

" After our return to England, as often as I happened to be on the Thames, I enquired of our watermen whether they were sensible of any difference in rowing over shallow or deep water. I found them all agreeing in the fact that there was a very great difference, but they differed widely in expressing the quantity of the difference ; some supposing it was equal to a mile in six, others to a mile in three. As I did not recollect to have met with any mention of this matter in our philosophical books, and conceiving that, if the difference should be really great, it might be an object of consideration in the many projects now on foot for digging new navigable canals in this island, I lately put my design of making the experiment in execution, in the following manner.

" I provided a trough of planed boards fourteen feet long, six inches wide, and six inches deep in the clear, filled with water within half an inch of the edge, to represent a canal. I had a loose board of nearly the same length and breadth, that being put into the water, might be sunk to any depth, and fixed by little wedges where I

would choose to have it stay, in order to make
different depths of water, leaving the surface at
the same hight with regard to the sides of the
trough. I had a little boat in form of a lighter
or boat of burden, six inches long, two inches
and a quarter wide, and one inch and a quarter
deep. When swimming it drew one inch of
water. To give motion to the boat, I fixed one
end of a long silk thread to its bow, just even
with the water's edge, the other end passed over
a well-made brass pulley, of about an inch in
diameter, turning freely upon a small axis; and
a shilling was the weight. Then placing the
boat at one end of the trough, the weight would
draw it through the water to the other. Not
having a watch that shows seconds, in order to
measure the time taken up by the boat in passing
from end to end of the trough, I counted as fast
as I could count to ten repeatedly, keeping an
account of the number of tens on my fingers.
And, as much as possible to correct any little in-
equalities in my counting, I repeated the experiment a number of times at each depth of water,
that I might take the medium."

The experiment proved the truth of the
boatmen's assertions. Franklin found that five
horses would be required to draw a boat in a
canal affording little more than enough water to
float it, which four horses could draw in a canal
of the proper depth.

No circumstance, remarks Mr. Parton, was
too trifling to engage him upon a series of experiments. At dinner, one day, a bottle of Madeira

was opened which had been bottled in Virginia many months before. Into the first glass poured from it fell three drowned flies. " Having heard it remarked that drowned flies were capable of being revived by the rays of the sun, I proposed making the experiment upon these; they were therefore exposed to the sun upon a sieve which had been employed to strain them out of the wine. In less than three hours two of them began by degrees to recover life. They commenced by some convulsive motions of the thighs, and at length they raised themselves upon their legs, wiped their eyes with their fore-feet, beat and brushed their wings with their hind feet, and soon after began to fly, finding themselves in Old England without knowing how they came thither. The third continued lifeless till sunset, when, losing all hopes of him, he was thrown away." And upon this he remarks: " I wish it were possible, from this instance, to invent a method of enbalming drowned persons in such a manner that they may be recalled to life at any period, however distant; for having a very ardent desire to see and observe the state of America a hundred years hence, I should prefer to any ordinary death being immersed in a cask of Madeira wine, with a few friends, till that time, to be then recalled to life by the solar warmth of my dear country."

Among the studies in natural philosophy of which but little is known to the general public may be mentioned Franklin's experiments with heat at a time when a thermometer was a scientific curiosity. The manner in which he proved that black cloth was not so good a covering for the body in hot weather as white, shows the simplicity of his methods and his faculty for making small means subserve great ends: "I took a number of little square pieces of broadcloth from a tailor's pattern-card, of various colors. There were black, deep blue, lighter blue, green, purple, red, yellow, white, and other colors or shades of colors. I laid them all out upon the snow in a bright sunshiny morning. In a few hours the black, being warmed most by the sun, was so low as to be below the stroke of the sun's rays; the dark blue almost as low, the lighter blue not quite so much as the dark, the other colors less as they were lighter, and the quite white remained on the surface of the snow, not having entered it at all. What signifies philosophy that does not apply to some use? May we not learn from hence that black clothes are not so fit to wear in a hot, sunny climate or season as white ones?" That all summer hats, particularly for soldiers, should be white, and that garden walls intended for fruit should be black, were suggestions put forth as a result of this experiment.

Dr. Small assigns to Franklin the credit of having discovered that repeated respiration imparts to air a poisonous quality similar to that which extinguishes candles and destroys life in mines and wells. "The doctor," he records, "breathed gently through a tube into a deep glass mug, so as to impregnate all the air in the mug with this quality. He then put a lighted *bougie* (candle) into the mug, and upon touching the air therein the flame was instantly extinguished; by frequently repeating this operation, the *bougie* gradually preserved its light longer in the mug, so as in a short time to retain it to the bottom of it, the air having totally lost the bad quality it had contracted from the breath blown into it." Upon being consulted with regard to the better ventilation of the House of Commons, he advised that openings should be made near the ceiling, communicating with flues running parallel with the chimneys and close enough to them to be kept warm by their heat. These flues, he recommended, should begin in the cellar, where the air was cool, and the flues being warmed by the hot air of the chimneys, would cause an upward current of air strong enough to expel the vitiated air in the upper part of the house. Franklin's letters at this time are full of the importance of ventilation. Unquestionably, he was among the first who called attention to the folly of excluding fresh air from hospitals and sick-rooms, particularly those of fever patients. As Mr. Parton expresses it, he cleared the pure air of heaven from calumnious imputation and threw open the windows of mankind.

Some inventions of Franklin's have not met with the approval of posterity. For instance, he seems to have had no more success with a reformed spelling of his own devising than laborers in the same field who came after him. He used to say that they alone spelt well who spelt ill, since the so-called bad speller used the letters according to their real value. The illiterate girl who wrote of her *bo* was more correct, he thought, than the young lady who would blush to omit a superfluous vowel. What was the use of the final letter in muff, and why take the trouble to write *tough* when *tuf* would do as well? Had he lived to see Dr. Webster's Dictionary, the lexicographer would have found in him an ardent champion. His reformed alphabet and spelling is an interesting curiosity, but hardly more. Some letters of our alphabet he omitted, only to add new ones. He also changed their order, making *o* the first letter and *m* the last. In this connection it may be well to say that Franklin was perhaps the first and foremost American champion of the movement, now so powerful, looking to the displacement of Latin and Greek as the foundations of education. At the very close of his life, in 1789, he issued his famous protest against the study of dead languages. He is reported to have said one evening, when talking about this matter: "When the custom of wearing broad cuffs with buttons first began, there was a reason for it; the cuffs might be brought down over the hands and thus guard them from wet and cold. But gloves came into use, and the broad cuffs were unnecessary; yet the custom was still retained. So likewise with cocked hats. The wide brim, when let down, afforded a protection from the rain and the sun. Umbrellas were introduced, yet fashion prevailed to keep cocked hats in vogue, although they were rather cumbersome than useful. Thus with the Latin language. When nearly all the books of Europe were written in that language, the study of it was essential in every system of education ; but it is now scarcely needed, except as an accomplishment, since it has everywhere given place, as a vehicle of thought and knowledge, to some one of the modern tongues."

With all his love of the practical, Franklin was not deficient in a rather delicate wit. I have already had occasion to quote at the beginning of this paper his disclaimer of the honors conferred upon him by Turgot's famous Latin line. Instances of this dry humor may be found all through Sparks's exhaustive biography. I remember one in particular. The merchants of Philadelphia, being at one time desirous to establish an assembly for dancing, they drew up some rules, among which was one " that no mechanic or mechanic's wife or daughter should be admitted on any terms." This rule being submitted to Franklin, he remarked that "it excluded God Almighty, for he was the greatest mechanic in the universe."

Benjamin Franklin's services to the cause of invention by no means ended with his own inventions. One of his greatest services was the part he took in the foundation of the American Philosophical Society, whose object was to bring into correspondence with a central association in Philadelphia all scientists, philosophers, and inventors on this continent and in Europe. Franklin's share in the foundation of this society, which has proved of such vast use, seems to have been largely overlooked by his biographers. Mr. Parton, having mentioned that Franklin founded the society in accordance with his proposal of 1743, adds : " The society was formed and continued in existence for some years. Nevertheless, its success was neither great nor permanent, for at that day the circle of men capable of taking much interest in science was too limited for the proper support of such an organization." The recent historian of the society, Dr. Robert M. Patterson, agrees, however, with Sparks in tracing the origin of the Philosophical Society, which grew into prominence about 1767, back to Franklin's proposal of 1743. After describing the Junto, or Leather Apron Society, formed among Franklin's acquaintance, a sort of debating club of eleven young men, Sparks says : " Forty years after its establishment it became the basis of the American Philosophical Society, of which Franklin was the first president, and the published transactions of which have contributed to the advancement of science and the diffusion of valuable knowledge in the United States." In his first proposal Franklin gave a list of the subjects that were to engage the attention of these New World philosophers. It included investigations in botany ; in medicine ; in mineralogy and mining ; in chemistry ; in mechanics ; in arts, trades, and manufactures ; in geography and topography ; in agriculture ; and, lest something should have been forgotten, he adds that the association should "give its attention to all philosophical experiments that let light into the nature of things, tend to increase the power of man over matter and multiply the

Franklin's Grave.

conveniences or pleasures of life." The duties of the secretary of the society were laid down and were arduous, including much foreign correspondence, in addition to the correcting, abstracting, and methodizing of such papers as required it. This office Franklin took upon himself.

While he lived the proceedings of the society scarcely ever failed of a useful end. Unlike so many original and inventive geniuses, his eminent common sense was as marked as his originality. In the language of his most recent biographer, John Bach McMaster, " whatever he has said on domestic economy or thrift is sound and striking. No other writer has left so many just and original observations on success in life. No other writer has pointed out so clearly the way to obtain the greatest amount of comfort out of life. What Solomon did for the spiritual man, that did Franklin for the earthly man. The book of Proverbs is a collection of receipts for laying up treasure in heaven. ' Poor Richard' is a collection of receipts for laying up treasure on earth."

II.

ROBERT FULTON.

ROBERT FULTON, the inventor of the steamboat, or at least the first man to apply the power of the steam-engine to the propulsion of boats in a practical and effective manner, was born in Little Britain, Lancaster County, Pa., 1765, of respectable but poor parents. His father was a native of Kilkenny, Ireland, and his mother came of a fairly well-to-do Irish family, settled in Pennsylvania. He was the third of five children. As a child he received the rudiments of a common education. His vocation showed itself in his earliest years. All his hours of recreation were passed in shops and in drawing. At the time he was seventeen he had become so much of an artist as to make money by portrait and landscape painting in Philadelphia, where he remained until he was twenty-one. After this he went to Washington County and there purchased a little farm on which he settled his mother, his father having died when he was three years old. He returned to Philadelphia, but on his way visited the Warm Springs of Pennsylvania, where he met with some gentlemen who were so much pleased with his painting that they advised him to go to England, where they told him he would meet with

Robert Fulton.

West who had then attained great celebrity. Fulton took this advice, and his reception by West, always kindly toward Americans, was such as he had been led to expect. The distinguished painter was so well pleased with him that he took him into his house, where he continued to live for several years. For some time Fulton made painting his chief employment, spending two years in Devonshire, near Exeter, where he made many influential acquaintances, among others the Duke of Bridgewater, famous for his canals, and Lord Stanhope, a nobleman noted for his love of science and his attachment to the mechanic arts. With Lord Stanhope, Fulton held a correspondence for a long time upon subjects in which they were interested.

In 1793, Fulton was engaged in a project to improve inland navigation. Even at that early day it appeared that he had conceived the idea of propelling vessels by steam, and he speaks in his letters of its practicability. In 1794 he obtained from the British Government a patent for improvements in canal locks, and his pursuits at this time appear to have been in this direction. In his preface to a description of his Nautilus, or "plunging" boat, a species of submarine boat, he says that he had resided eighteen months in Birmingham where he acquired much of his knowledge of mechanics. In later years, when in Paris, Fulton sent a large collection of his manuscripts to this country. Unfortunately, the vessel in which they were sent was wrecked, and, while the case was recovered, only a few fragments of the manuscripts could be used. It is owing to this misfortune that we have so few records of Fulton's work at this time.

We know, however, that in 1794 he submitted to the British Society for the Promotion of Arts and Commerce an improvement of his invention for sawing marble, for which he received the

Birthplace of Robert Fulton.*

thanks of the society and an honorary medal. He invented also, it is thought, about this time, a machine for spinning flax and another for making ropes, for both of which he obtained patents from the British Government. A mechanical contrivance for scooping out earth to form channels for canals or aqueducts, which is said to have

* This illustration and the four following are from Knox's " Life of Fulton," reproduced by permission of the publishers, G. P. Putnam's Sons.

been much used in England, was also his invention. The subject of canals appears to have chiefly engaged his attention during these years of the end of the century. He called himself a civil engineer, and under this title published his work on canals, and, in 1795, many essays on the same subject in one of the London journals. He recommended small canals and boats of little burden in a treatise on "Improvement of Canal Navigation," and inclined planes instead of locks, as a means of transporting canal boats from one level to another. His plans were strongly recommended by the British Board of Agriculture. Throughout his course as civil engineer his talent for drawing was of great advantage to him, and the plates annexed to his works are admirable examples of such work. He seems to have neglected his painting till a short time before his death, when he took up the brush again to paint some portraits of his family. During his residence in England he sent copies of his works to distinguished men in this country, setting forth the advantages to be derived from communication by canals.

Having obtained a patent for mill improvements from the British Government, he went to France with the intention of introducing his invention there; but, not meeting with much encouragement, he devoted his time to other matters. Political economy had also some attraction for him, and he wrote a book to show that internal improvements would have a good effect on the happiness of a nation. He not only

4

wished to see a free and speedy communication between the different parts of a large country, but universal free trade between all countries. He thought that it would take ages to establish the freedom of the seas by the common consent of nations, and believed in destroying ships of war, so as to put it out of the power of any nation to control ocean trade. In 1797 he became acquainted with Joel Barlow, the well-known American, then residing in Paris, in whose family he lived for seven years, during which time he learned French and something of German, and studied mathematics and chemistry. In the same year he made an experiment with Mr. Barlow on the Seine with a machine he had constructed to give packages of gunpowder a progressive motion under water and then to explode at a given point. These experiments appear to have been the first in the line of his submarine boats, and are unquestionably the germ of all subsequent inventions in the direction of torpedo warfare.

Want of money to carry out his designs induced him to apply to the French Directory, who at first gave him reason to expect their aid, but finally rejected his plan. Fulton, however, was not to be discouraged, but went on with his inventions, and having made a handsome model of his machine for destroying ships, a commission was appointed to examine his plans, but they also rejected them. He offered his idea to the British Government, still again without success, although a committee was appointed to examine his models. The French Government being changed, and Bonaparte having come to the head of it, Fulton presented an address to him. A commission was appointed, and some assistance given which enabled him to put some of his plans into practice. In the spring of 1801 he went to Brest to make experiments with the plunging boat that he had constructed in the winter. This, as he says, had many imperfections, to be expected in a first machine, and had been injured by rust, as parts which should have been of copper or brass were made of iron.

Notwithstanding these disadvantages, he engaged in a course of experiments which required no less courage than perseverance. From a report of his proceedings to the committee appointed by the French Government we learn that in July, 1801, he embarked with three companions on board of this boat, in the harbor of Brest, and descended to the depth of twenty-five feet, remaining below the surface an hour, in utter darkness, as the candles were found to consume too much of the vital air. He placed two men at the engine, which was intended to give her motion, and one at the helm, while he, with a barometer before him, kept her balanced between the upper and lower waters. He could turn her round while under the water, and found that in seven minutes he had gone about a third of a mile. During that summer Fulton descended under water with a store of air compressed into a copper globe, whereby he was enabled to remain under water four hours and twenty minutes. The success of these experiments determined him to try the effect of his invention on the English war-ships, then daily near the harbor of Brest—France and England being then at war. He made his own bombs. For experimental purposes a small vessel was anchored in the harbor, and with a bomb containing about twenty pounds of powder, he approached within about two hundred yards, struck the vessel, and blew her into atoms. A column of water and fragments were sent nearly one hundred feet into the air. This experiment was made in the presence of the prefect of the department and a multitude of spectators. During the summer of 1801 Fulton tried to use his bombs against some of the English vessels, but was not successful in getting within range. The French Government refused to give him further encouragement.

The English had some information concerning the attempts that their enemies were making, and the anxiety expressed induced the British Minister to communicate with Fulton and try to secure to England his services. In this he was successful, and Fulton went to London, where he arrived in 1804, and met Pitt and Lord Melville. When Mr. Pitt first saw a drawing of a torpedo with a sketch of the mode of applying it, and understood what would be the effect of the explosion, he said that if it were introduced into practice it could not fail to annihilate all navies.

But from the subsequent conduct of the British ministry it is supposed that they never really intended to give Fulton a fair opportunity to try

the effect of his submarine engines. Their object may have been to prevent these devices
getting into the hands of an enemy. Several
experiments were made, and some of them were
failures, but on October 15, 1805, he blew up a
strong-built Danish brig of two hundred tons
burden, which had been provided for the experiment and which was anchored near the residence

Fulton Blowing Up a Danish Brig.

of Pitt. The torpedo used on this occasion contained one hundred and seventy pounds of powder. In fifteen minutes from the time of starting
the machinery the explosion took place. It lifted
the brig almost entire and broke her completely
in two; in one minute nothing was to be seen of
her but floating fragments. Notwithstanding
the complete success of this experiment, the
British ministry seems to have had nothing to do
with Fulton. The inventor was rather discour-

aged at this lack of appreciation and, after some further experiments, he sailed for New York in December, 1806.

In this country Fulton devoted himself at once to his projects of submarine warfare and steam navigation. So far from being discouraged by his failure to impress Europe with the importance of his torpedoes, his confidence was unshaken, because he saw that his failures were to be attributed to trivial errors that could easily be corrected. He induced our Government to give him the means of making further experiments, and invited the magistracy of New York and a number of citizens to Governor's Island where were the torpedoes and the machinery with which his experiments were to be made. In July, 1807, he blew up, in the harbor of New York, a large brig prepared for that purpose. He also devised at this time a number of stationary torpedoes, really casks of powder, with triggers that might be caught by the keel of any passing vessel. In March, 1810, $5,000 were granted by Congress for further experiments in submarine explosions. The sloop of war. Argus, was prepared for defence against the torpedoes after Fulton had explained his mode of attack. This defence was so complete that Fulton found it impracticable to do anything with his torpedoes. Some experiments were made, however, with a gun-harpoon and cable cutter, and after several attempts a fourteen-inch cable was cut off several feet below the surface of the water.

Fulton was, during all these experiments, much pressed for money, and apparently was making no headway toward the use of his submarine engines in a profitable way. It was in despair of getting our Government to make an investment in this direction that he finally turned to the problem of navigation by steam. He had the valuable co-operation in his new work of Chancellor Livingston, of New Jersey, who, while devoting much of his own time and means to the advancement of science, was fond of fostering the discoveries of others. He had very clear conceptions of what would be the great advantages of steamboats on the navigable rivers of the United States. He had already, when in Paris, applied himself at great expense to constructing vessels and machinery for that kind of navigation. As early as 1798 he believed that he had accomplished his object, and represented to the Legislature of New York that he was possessed of a mode of applying the steam-engine to a boat on new and advantageous principles ; but that he was deterred from carrying it into effect by the uncertainty of expensive experiments, unless he could be assured of an exclusive advantage should it be successful. The Legislature in March, 1798, passed an act vesting him with the exclusive right and privilege of navigating all kinds of boats which might be propelled by the force of fire or steam on all the waters within the territory of New York for the term of twenty years, upon condition that he should within a twelve-month build such a boat, whose progress should not be less than four miles an hour.

Livingston, as soon as the act had passed, built a boat of about thirty tons burden, to be pro-

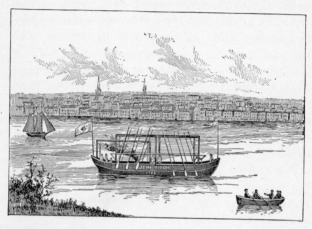

John Fitch's Steamboat at Philadelphia.

pelled by steam. Soon after he entered into a contract with Fulton, by which it was agreed that a patent should be taken out in the United States in Fulton's name. Thus began the preparations for the first practical steamboat. All the experiments were paid for by Chancellor Livingston, but the work was Fulton's. In 1802, in Paris, he began a course of calculations upon the resistance of water, upon the most advantageous form of the body to be moved, and upon the different means of propelling vessels which had been previously attempted. After a variety of calculations he rejected the proposed plan of using paddles or oars, such as those already used by Fitch; likewise that of ducks' feet, which open as they are pushed out and shut as they are drawn in; also that of forcing water out of the stern of the vessel. He retained two methods as worthy of experiment, namely, end- less chains with paddle-boards upon them, and the paddle-wheel. The latter was found to be the most promising, and was finally adopted after a number of trials with models on a little river which runs through the village of Plom- bières, to which he had retired in the spring of 1802, to pursue his experiments without inter- ruption.

It was now determined to build an experimen-

Fulton's First Experiment with Paddle-wheels.

tal boat, which was completed in the spring of 1803; but when Fulton was on the point of mak- ing an experiment with her, an accident hap- pened to the boat, the woodwork not having been framed strongly enough to bear the weight of the machinery and the agitation of the river. The accident did the machinery very little injury; but they were obliged to build the boat almost entirely anew. She was completed in July; her length was sixty-six feet and she was eight feet wide. Early in August, Fulton addressed a letter to the French National Institute, inviting the members to witness a trial of his boat, which was made before the members, and in the presence of a great multitude of Parisians. The experiment was entirely satisfactory to Fulton, though the boat did not move altogether with as much speed as he expected. But he imputed her moving so slowly to the extremely defective machinery, and to imperfections which were to be expected in the first experiment with so complicated a machine; the defects were such as might be easily remedied.

Such entire confidence did he acquire from this experiment that immediately afterward he wrote to Messrs. Boulton & Watt, of Birmingham, England, ordering certain parts of a steam-engine to be made for him, and sent to America. He did not disclose to them for what purpose the engine was intended, but his directions were such as would produce the parts of an engine that might be put together within a compass suited for a boat. Mr. Livingston had written to his friends in this country, and through their assistance an act was passed by the Legislature of the State of New York, on April 5, 1803, by which the rights and exclusive privileges of navigating all the waters of that State, by vessels propelled by fire or steam, granted to Livingston by the Act of 1798, as already mentioned, were extended to Livingston and Fulton, for the term of twenty years from the date of the new act. By this law the time of producing proof of the practicability of propelling by steam a boat of twenty tons capacity, at the rate of four miles an hour, with and against the ordinary current of the Hudson, was extended two years, and by a subsequent law, the time was extended to 1807.

Very soon after Fulton's arrival in New York he began building his first American boat. While she was constructing, he found that her cost would greatly exceed his calculations. He endeavored to lessen the pressure on his own finances by offering one-third of the rights for a proportionate contribution to the expense. It was generally known that he made this offer, but no one was then willing to afford aid to his enterprise.

In the spring of 1807, Fulton's first American boat was launched from the shipyard of Charles Brown, on the East River. The engine from England was put on board, and in August she was completed, and was moved by her machinery from her birthplace to the Jersey shore. Livingston and Fulton had invited many of their friends to witness the first trial, among them Dr. Mitchell and Dr. M'Neven, to whom we are indebted for some account of what

passed on this occasion. Nothing could exceed
the surprise and admiration of all who wit-
nessed the experiment. The minds of the most
incredulous were changed in a few minutes.
Before the boat had gone a quarter of a mile,
the greatest unbeliever must have been converted. The man who, while he looked on the
expensive machine, thanked his stars that he
had more wisdom than to waste his money on
such idle schemes, changed his mind as the boat
moved from the wharf and gained speed, and
his complacent expression gradually stiffened
into one of wonder.

This boat, which was called the Clermont,
soon after made a trip to Albany. Fulton gives
the following account of this voyage in a letter
to his friend, Mr. Barlow:

"My steamboat voyage to Albany and back,
has turned out rather more favorable than I had
calculated. The distance from New York to
Albany is one hundred and fifty miles; I ran
it up in thirty-two hours, and down in thirty.
I had a light breeze against me the whole way,
both going and coming, and the voyage has been
performed wholly by the power of the steam-
engine. I overtook many sloops and schooners
beating to windward, and parted with them as if
they had been at anchor. The power of propelling boats by steam is now fully proved. The
morning I left New York there were not, perhaps,
thirty persons in the city who believed that the
boat would even move one mile an hour, or be of
the least utility; and while we were putting off

Departure of the Clermont on her First Voyage.

from the wharf, which was crowded with spectators, I heard a number of sarcastic remarks.
This is the way in which ignorant men compliment what they call philosophers and projectors.
Having employed much time, money, and zeal, in
accomplishing this work, it gives me, as it will
you, great pleasure to see it fully answer my expectations. It will give a cheap and quick con-
veyance to the merchandise on the Mississippi,
Missouri, and other great rivers, which are now
laying open their treasures to the enterprise
of our countrymen; and although the prospect
of personal emolument has been some induce-
ment to me, yet I feel infinitely more pleasure in
reflecting on the immense advantage that my
country will derive from the invention."

Soon after this successful voyage, the Hudson
boat was advertised and established as a regular
passage-boat between New York and Albany.
She, however, in the course of the season, met
with several accidents, from the hostility of
those engaged in the ordinary navigation of the
river, and from defects in her machinery, the
greatest of which was having her water-wheel
shafts of cast-iron, which was insufficient to sustain the great power applied to them. The
wheels also were hung without any support for
the outward end of the shaft, which is now
supplied by what are called the wheel-guards.

At the session of 1808 a law was passed to
prolong the time of the exclusive right to thirty
years; it also declared combinations to destroy
the boat, or wilful attempts to injure her, public

offences, punishable by fine and imprisonment. Notwithstanding her misfortunes, the boat continued to run as a packet, always loaded with passengers, for the remainder of the summer. In the course of the ensuing winter she was enlarged, and in the spring of 1808 she again began running as a packet-boat, and continued it through the season. Several other boats were soon built for the Hudson River, and also for steamboat companies formed in different parts of the United States. On February 11, 1809, Fulton took out a patent for his inventions in navigation by steam, and on February 9, 1811, he obtained a second patent for some improvements in his boats and machinery.

About the year 1812 two steam ferry-boats were built under the direction of Fulton for crossing the Hudson River, and one of the same description for the East River. These boats were what are called twin-boats, each of them being two complete hulls united by a deck or bridge. They were sharp at both ends, and moved equally well with either end foremost, so that they crossed and recrossed without losing any time by turning about. He contrived, with great ingenuity, floating docks for the reception of these boats, and a means by which they were brought to them without a shock. These boats, were the first of a fleet which has since carried hundreds of millions of passengers to and from New York.

From the time the first boat was put in motion till the death of Fulton, the art of navigating by steam advanced rapidly to that perfection of which he believed it capable; the boats performed each successive trip with increased speed, and every year improvements were made. The last boat built by Fulton was invariably the best, the most convenient, and the swiftest.

At the beginning of 1814 a number of the citizens of New York, alarmed at the exposed situation of their harbor, had assembled with a view to consider whether some measures might not be taken to aid the Government in its protection. This assembly had some knowledge of Fulton's plans for submarine attack, and knew that he contemplated other means of defence. It deputed a number of gentlemen to act for it, and these were called the Coast and Harbor Committee. Fulton exhibited to this committee the model and plans for a vessel of war, to be propelled by steam, capable of carrying a strong battery, with furnaces for red-hot shot, and which, he represented, would move at the rate of four miles an hour. The confidence of the committee in this design was confirmed by the opinions of many of our most distinguished naval commanders, which he had obtained in writing, and exhibited to the committee. They pointed out many advantages which a steam vessel of war would possess over those with sails only.

The National Legislature passed a law in March, 1814, authorizing the President of the United States to cause to be built, equipped, and employed one or more floating batteries for the defence of the waters of the United States. A sub-committee of five gentlemen was appointed to superintend the building of the proposed vessel, and Fulton, whose spirit animated the whole enterprise, was appointed the engineer. In June, 1814, the keel of this novel and mighty engine was laid, and in October she was launched from the New York yard of Adam and Noah Brown. The scene exhibited on this occasion was magnificent. It happened on one of our bright autumnal days. Multitudes of spectators crowded the surrounding shores. The river and bay were filled with vessels of war, dressed in all their colors in compliment to the occasion. By May, 1815, her engine was put on board, and she was so far completed as to afford an opportunity of trying her machinery. On the 4th of July, in the same year, the steam-frigate made a passage to the ocean and back, a distance of fifty-three miles, in eight hours and twenty minutes, by the mere force of steam. In September she made another passage to the sea, and having at this time the weight of her whole armament on board, she went at the rate of five and a half miles an hour, upon an average, with and against the tide. The superintending committee gave in their report a full description of the Fulton the First, the honored name this vessel bore.

The last work in which the active and ingenious mind of Fulton was engaged was a project for the modification of his submarine boat. He presented a model of this vessel to the Gov-

ernment, by which it was approved; and under
Federal authority he began building one; but
before the hull was entirely finished his country

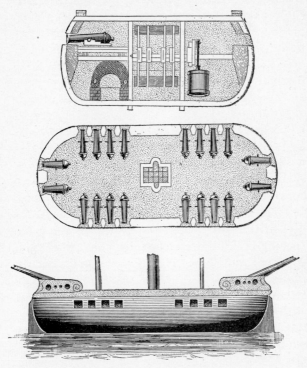

The "Demologos," or "Fulton the First."
The first steam vessel-of-war in the world.

had to lament his death, and the mechanics he
employed were incapable of proceeding without
him.

During the whole time that Fulton had thus
been devoting his talents to the service of his

5

country, he had been harassed by lawsuits and controversies with those who were violating his patent rights, or intruding upon his exclusive grants. The State of New Jersey had passed a law which operated against Fulton, without being of much advantage to those interested in its passage, inasmuch as the laws of New York prevented any but Fulton's boats to approach the city of New York. Its only operation was to stop a boat owned in New York, which had been for several years running to New Brunswick, under a license from Messrs. Livingston and Fulton. A bold attempt was therefore made to induce the Legislature of the State of New York to repeal the laws which they had passed for the protection of their exclusive grant to Livingston and Fulton. The committee reported that such repeal might be passed consistently with good faith, honor, and justice! This report being made to the House, it was prevailed upon to be less precipitate than the committee had been. It gave time, which the committee would not do, for Fulton to be sent for from New York. The Assembly and Senate in joint session examined witnesses, and heard him and the petitioner by counsel. The result was that the Legislature refused to repeal the prior law, or to pass any act on the subject. The Legislature of the State of New Jersey also repealed their law, which left Fulton in the full enjoyment of his rights. This enjoyment was of very short duration; for on returning from Trenton, after this last trial, he was exposed on the Hudson, which was very full of ice, for several hours. He had not a constitution to encounter such exposure, and upon his return found himself much indisposed. He had at that time great anxiety about the steam-frigate, and, after confining himself to the house for a few days, went to give his superintendence to the workmen employed about her. Forgetting his ill-health in the interest he took in what was doing on the frigate, he remained too long exposed on a bad day to the weather. He soon felt the effects of this imprudence. His indisposition returned upon him with such violence as to confine him to his bed. His illness increased, and on February 24, 1815, it ended his life.

It was not known that Fulton's illness was dangerous till a very short time before his death. Means were immediately taken to testify, publicly, the universal regret at his loss, and respect for his memory. The corporation of the city of New York, the different literary institutions and other societies, assembled and passed resolutions expressing their estimation of his worth, and regret at his loss. They also resolved to attend his funeral, and that the members should wear badges of mourning for a certain time. As soon as the Legislature, which was then in session at Albany, heard of the death of Fulton, they expressed their participation in the general sentiment by resolving that the members of both Houses should wear mourning for some weeks.

In 1806 Fulton married Harriet Livingston, a daughter of Walter Livingston, a relative of his associate, Chancellor Livingston. He left four children ; one son, Robert Barlow Fulton, and three daughters. Fulton was in person considerably above medium height; his face showed great intelligence. Natural refinement and long intercourse with the most polished society of Europe and America had given him grace and elegance of manner.

The Clermont.

III.

ELI WHITNEY.

In 1784 an American vessel arrived at Liverpool having on board, as part of her cargo, eight bags of cotton, which were seized by the Custom-House under the conviction that they could not be the growth of America. The whole amount of cotton arriving at Liverpool from America during the two following years was less than one hundred and twenty bags. When Eli Whitney, the inventor of the cotton-gin, applied for his first patent in 1793, the total export of cotton from the United States was less than ten thousand bales. Fifty years later, the growth of this industry, owing almost wholly to Whitney's gin, had increased to millions of bales, and by 1860, the export amounted to four million bales.

According to the estimate of Judge Johnson, given in the most famous decision affecting the cotton-gin, the debts of the South were paid off by its aid, its capital was increased, and its lands trebled in value. This famous device, the gift of a young Northerner to the South, was rewarded by thirty years of ingratitude, relieved only by a few gleams of sunshine in the way of justice, serving to make the injustice all the more conspicuous. Whitney added hundreds of millions to the wealth of the United States.

Eli Whitney.

His personal reward was countless lawsuits and endless vexation of body and spirit. No more conspicuous example can be cited of steady patience and sweet-tempered perseverance.

Eli Whitney was born in Westborough, Worcester County, Mass., December 8, 1765. His parents belonged to that respectable class of society who, by honest farming and kindred industries, managed to provide well for the rising family—the class from whom have arisen most of those who in New England have attained to eminence and usefulness. The indications of his mechanical genius were noted at an early age. Of his passion for mechanics, his sister gives the following account :

" Our father had a workshop and sometimes made wheels of different kinds, and chairs. He had a variety of tools and a lathe for turning chair-posts. This gave my brother an opportunity of learning the use of tools when very young. He lost no time, but as soon as he could handle tools he was always making something in the shop, and seemed to prefer that to work on the farm. After the death of our mother, when our father had been absent from home two or three days, on his return he inquired of the housekeeper what the boys had been doing. She told him what the elders had done. ' But what has Eli been doing ? ' said he. She replied he has been making a fiddle. ' Ah ! ' added he, despondently, ' I fear Eli will have to take his portion in fiddles.' "

He was at this time about twelve years old. The sister adds that his fiddle was finished throughout like a common violin and made pretty good music. It was examined by many persons, and all pronounced it to be a model piece of work for such a boy. From this time he was always employed to repair violins, and did many nice jobs that were executed to the entire satisfaction and even to the astonishment of his customers. His father's watch being the greatest piece of mechanism that had yet presented itself to his observation, he was extremely desirous of examining its interior construction, but was not permitted to do so. One Sunday morning, observing that his father was going to church and would leave at home the wonderful little machine, he feigned illness as an apology for not going. As soon as the family were out of sight, he flew to the room where the watch hung and took it down. He was so delighted with its motion that he took it to pieces before he thought of the consequences of his rash deed; for his father was a stern parent, and punishment would have been the reward of his idle curiosity, had the mischief been detected. He, however, put the works so neatly together that his father never discovered his audacity until he himself told him many years afterward.

When Eli was thirteen years old his father married a second time. His stepmother, among her articles of furniture, had a handsome set of table-knives that she valued very highly.

One day Eli said: " I could make as good ones

if I had tools, and I could make the tools if I had common tools to begin with;" his mother laughed at him. But it so happened soon afterward that one of the knives was broken, and he made one exactly like it in every respect, except the stamp of the blade. When he was fifteen or sixteen years of age, he suggested to his father an enterprise which clearly showed his capacity for important work. The time being the Revolutionary War, nails were in great demand and at high prices. They were made chiefly by hand. Whitney proposed to his father to get him a few tools and allow him to set up the manufacture of nails. His father consented, and the work was begun. By extraordinary diligence he found time to make tools for his own use and to put in knife-blades, repair farm machinery, and perform other little jobs beyond the skill of the country workman. At this occupation the enterprising boy worked alone with great success and with large profit to his father for two winters, going on with the ordinary work of the farm during the summer. He devised a plan for enlarging the business, and managed to obtain help from a fellow-laborer whom he picked up when on a short journey of forty miles, in the course of which he tells us that he called at every workshop on the way and gleaned all the information as to tools and methods that he could.

At the close of the war the business of making nails was no longer profitable; but the fashion prevailing among the ladies of fastening on their bonnets with long pins having appeared, he contrived to make these pins with such skill that he nearly monopolized the business, though he devoted to it only such leisure as he could redeem from the occupations of the farm. He also made excellent walking-canes. At the age of nineteen Whitney conceived the idea of getting a liberal education; and partly by the results of his mechanical industries, and partly by teaching the village school, he was enabled so far to surmount the difficulties in his way as to prepare himself for the Freshman Class in Yale College, which he entered in 1789. At college his mechanical propensity frequently showed itself. He successfully undertook, on one occasion, the repairing of some of the philosophical apparatus. Soon after taking his degree, in the autumn of 1792, he engaged with a Georgia family as private teacher, and through his engagement he made the acquaintance of a certain General Greene, of Savannah, who took a deep interest in him, and with whom he began the study of law. While living with the Greenes he noticed an embroidery-frame used by Mrs. Greene, and about which she complained, observing that it tore the delicate threads of her work. Young Whitney, eager to oblige his hostess, went to work and speedily produced a frame on an entirely new plan. The family were much delighted with it, and considered it a wonderful piece of ingenuity.

Not long afterward the Greenes were visited by a party of gentlemen, chiefly officers who had served under the general in the Revolutionary

War. The conversation turned on the state of agriculture. It was remarked that unfortunately there was no means of cleaning the staple of the green cotton-seed, which might otherwise be profitably raised on land unsuitable for rice. But until someone devised a machine which would clean the cotton, it was vain to think of raising

Whitney Watching the Cotton-Gin.

it for market. Separating one pound of the clean staple from the seed was a day's work for a woman. The time usually devoted to the picking of cotton was the evening, after the labor of the field was over. Then the slaves—men, women, and children—were collected in circles, with one in the middle whose duty it was to rouse the dosing and quicken the indolent. While the company were engaged in this conversation, Mrs. Greene said: "Gentlemen, apply to my young friend here, Mr. Whitney ; he can make anything." And she showed them the frame and several other articles he had made. He modestly disclaimed all pretensions to mechanical genius, and replied that he had never seen cotton-seed.

Nevertheless, he immediately began upon the task of inventing and constructing the machine on which his fame depends. A Mr. Phineas Miller, a neighbor, to whom he communicated his design, warmly encouraged him, and gave him a room in his house wherein to carry on his operations. Here he began work with the disadvantage of being obliged to manufacture his own tools and draw his own wire—an article not to be found in Savannah. Mr. Miller and Mrs. Greene were the only persons who knew anything of his occupation. Near the close of the winter, 1793, the machine was so far completed as to leave no doubt of its success. The person who contributed most to the success of the undertaking, after the inventor, was his friend, Miller, a native of Connecticut and a graduate of Yale. Like Whitney, he had come to Georgia as a private teacher, and after the death of General Greene he married the widow. He was a lawyer by profession, with a turn for mechanics. He had some money and proposed to Whitney to become his partner, he to be at the whole expense of manufacturing the invention until it should be patented. If the machine should succeed, they agreed that the profits and advantages should be divided between them. A

legal paper covering this agreement and estab-
lishing the firm of Miller & Whitney, bears the
date of May 27, 1793.

An invention so important to the agricultural
interests of the country could not long remain a
secret. The knowledge of it swept through the
State, and so great was the excitement on the
subject that crowds of persons came from all
parts to see the machine; it was not deemed safe
to gratify curiosity until the patent-right should
be secured. But so determined were some of
these people that neither law nor justice could
restrain them; they broke into the building by
night and carried off the machine. In this way
the public became possessed of the invention,
and before Whitney could complete his model
and secure his patent, a number of machines,
patterned after his, were in successful operation.

The principle of the Whitney cotton-gin and
all other gins following its features is so well
known as to make it scarcely worth while to de-
scribe it here. The different parts are two cylinders of different diameters, mounted in a strong
wooden frame, one cylinder bearing a number
of circular saws fitted into grooves cut into the
cylinder. The other hollow cylinder is mounted
with brushes, the tips of whose bristles touch
the saw-teeth. The cotton is put into a hopper,
where it is met by the sharp teeth of the saws,
torn from the seed, and carried to a point where
the brushes sweep it off into a convenient recep-
tacle. The seeds are too large to pass between
the bars through which the saws protrude. This

is the principle of the first machine, but many improvements have been made since Whitney's day. Nevertheless, by means of the cotton-gin, even in its earliest shape, one man, with the aid of two-horse power, could clean five thousand pounds of cotton in a day.

The Cotton-Gin.
(From the original model.)

As soon as the partnership of Miller & Whitney was formed, the latter went to Connecticut to perfect the machine, obtain the patent, and manufacture for Georgia as many machines as he thought would supply the demand. At once there began between Whitney in Connecticut and Miller in Georgia a correspondence relative to the cotton-gin, which gives a complete history of the extraordinary efforts made by the two partners and the disappointments that fell to their lot. The very first letter, written three days after Whitney left, announces that encroachments upon their rights had already begun. "It will be necessary," says Miller, "to have a considerable number of gins in readiness to send out as soon as the patent is obtained in order to satisfy the absolute demands and make people's heads easy on the subject; for I am informed of two other claimants for the honor of the invention of the cotton-gin in addition to those we knew before." At the close of the year 1793 Whitney was to return to Georgia with his gins, where his partner had made arrangements for beginning business. The importunity of Miller's letters, written during this period, urging him to come on, show how eager the Georgia planters were to enter the new field of enterprise that the genius of Whitney had opened to them. Nor did they at first contemplate stealing the invention. But the minds of even the more honorable among the planters were afterward deluded by various artifices set on foot by designing rivals of Whitney with a view to robbing him of his rights. One of the greatest difficulties experienced by the partners was the extreme scarcity of money, which embarrassed them so much as to make it impossible to construct machines fast enough.

In April Whitney returned to Georgia. Large crops of cotton had been planted, the

profits of which were to depend almost wholly
on the success of the gin. A formidable com-
petitor, the roller-gin, had also appeared, which
destroyed the seed by means of rollers, crushing
them between revolving cylinders instead of dis-
engaging them by means of teeth. The fragments of seeds which remained in the cotton
made it much inferior to Whitney's gin, and it
was slower in operation. A still more dangerous rival appeared in 1795, under the name of
the saw-gin. It was really Whitney's invention,
except that the teeth were cut in circular rings
of iron instead of being made of wire, as in the
earlier forms of the Whitney gin. The use of
such teeth had occurred to Whitney, as he established by legal proof. They would have been
of no use except in connection with other parts
of his machine, and it was a palpable attempt to
invade his patent right. It was chiefly in reference to this device that the endless lawsuits that
wore the life out of the partners were afterward
held.

In March, 1795, after two years of struggle,
during which no progress seems to have been
made, although the value of the gin was proved,
Whitney went to New York, where he was de-
tained three weeks by fever. Upon reaching
New Haven he discovered that his shop, with
all his machines and papers, had been consumed
by fire. Thus he was suddenly reduced to bank-
ruptcy and was in debt $4,000 without any means
of payment. He was not, however, one to sink
under such trials. Miller showed the same buoy-

ant spirit, and the following extract of a letter of
his to Whitney may be a useful lesson to young
men in trouble :

" I think we ought to meet such events with
equanimity. We have been pursuing a valuable
object by honorable means, and I trust that all
our measures have been such as reason and virt-
ue must justify. It has pleased Providence to
postpone the attainment of this object. In the
midst of the reflections which your story has suggested, and with feelings keenly awake to the
heavy, the extensive injury we have sustained, I
feel a secret joy and satisfaction that you possess a mind in this respect similar to my own—
that you are not disheartened, that you do not
relinquish the pursuit, and that you will perse-
vere, and endeavor, at all events, to attain the
main object. This is exactly consonant to my
own determinations. I will devote all my time,
all my thoughts, all my exertions, and all the
money I can earn or borrow to encompass and
complete the business we have undertaken ; and if
fortune should, by any future disaster, deny us the
boon we ask, we will at least deserve it. It shall
never be said that we have lost an object which
a little perseverance could have attained. I think,
indeed, it will be very extraordinary if two young
men in the prime of life, with some share of ingenuity, and with a little knowledge of the world, a
great deal of industry, and a considerable com-
mand of property, should not be able to sustain
such a stroke of misfortune as this, heavy as it is."

6

Miller winds up by suggesting to Whitney that perhaps he can get help in New Haven by offering twelve per cent. a year for money with which to build a new shop, and the inventor seems to have had some success in reorganizing his affairs, even under such desperate conditions. Word came at the same time from England that manufacturers had condemned the cotton cleaned by their machines on the ground that the staple was greatly injured. This threatened a death-blow to their hopes. At the time, 1796, they already had thirty gins at different places in Georgia, some worked by horses and oxen and some by water. Some of these were still standing a few years ago. The following extract of a letter by Whitney will show the state of his mind and affairs:

" The extreme embarrassments which have been for a long time accumulating upon me are now become so great that it will be impossible for me to struggle against them many days longer. It has required my utmost exertions to exist without making the least progress in our business. I have labored hard against the strong current of disappointment which has been threatening to carry us down the cataract, but I have labored with a shattered oar and struggled in vain, unless some speedy relief is obtained. . . . Life is but short at best, and six or seven years out of the midst of it is to him who makes it an immense sacrifice. My most unremitted attention has been devoted to our business. I have sacrificed to it other objects from which, before this time, I might certainly have gained $20,000 or $30,000. My whole prospects have been embarked in it, with the expectation that I should before this time have realized something from it."

The cotton of Whitney's gin was, however, sought by merchants in preference to other kinds, and respectable manufacturers testified in his favor. Had it not been for the extensive and shameful violations of their patent-right, the partners might yet have succeeded; but these encroachments had become so extensive as almost to destroy its value. The issue of the first important trial that they were able to obtain on the merits of the gin is announced in the following letter from Miller to Whitney, dated May 11, 1797:

" The event of the first patent suit, after all our exertions made in such a variety of ways, has gone against us. The preposterous custom of trying civil causes of this intricacy and magnitude by a common jury, together with the imperfection of the patent law, frustrated all our views, and disappointed expectations which had become very sanguine. The tide of popular opinion was running in our favor, the judge was well disposed toward us, and many decided friends were with us, who adhered firmly to our cause and interests. The judge gave a charge to the jury pointedly in our favor; after which the defendant himself told an acquaintance of his that he would give two thousand dollars to be free from the verdict, and yet the jury gave it against us, after a consultation of about an hour. And having made the verdict general, no appeal would lie.

" On Monday morning, when the verdict was rendered, we applied for a new trial, but the judge refused it to us on the ground that the jury might have made up their opinion on the defect of the law, which makes an aggression consist of making, devising, and using or selling; whereas we could only charge the defendant with using.

"Thus, after four years of assiduous labor, fatigue, and difficulty, are we again set afloat by a new and most unexpected obstacle. Our hopes of success are now removed to a period still more distant than before, while our expenses are realized beyond all controversy."

Great efforts were made to obtain trial in a second suit in Savannah the following May, and a number of witnesses were collected from various parts of the country, all to no purpose, for the judge failed to appear, and in the meantime, owing to the failure of the first suit, encroachments on the patent-right had multiplied prodigiously.

In April, 1799, nearly a year later, and two years after their first legal rebuff, Miller writes as follows:

"The prospect of making anything by ginning in this State is at an end. Surreptitious gins are erected in every part of the country, and the

jurymen at Augusta have come to an understanding among themselves that they will never
give a cause in our favor, let the merits of the
case be as they may."

The company would now have gladly relin-
quished the plan of making their own machines,
and confined their operations to the sale of patent-
rights ; but few would buy the right to a machine
which could be used with impunity without purchase, and those few usually gave notes instead
of cash, which they afterward, to a great extent,
avoided paying, either by obtaining a verdict
from the juries declaring them void, or by con-
triving to postpone the collection till they were
barred by the Statute of Limitations, a period of
only four years. The agent of Miller & Whitney, who was despatched on a collecting tour
through the State of Georgia, informed his em-
ployers that such obstacles were thrown in his
way by one or the other of these causes that he
was unable to collect money enough to pay his
expenses. It was suggested that an application
to the Legislature of South Carolina to purchase
the patent-right for that State would be successful. Whitney accordingly repaired to Colum-
bia, and the business was brought before the
Legislature in December, 1801. An extract from
a letter by Whitney at this time shows the nature of the contract thus made :

" I have been at this place a little more than
two weeks attending the Legislature. A few
hours previous to their adjournment they voted

to purchase for the State of South Carolina my patent-right to the machine for cleaning cotton at $50,000, of which sum $20,000 is to be paid in hand, and the remainder in three annual payments of $10,000 each." He adds: "We get but a song for it in comparison with the worth of the thing, but it is securing something. It will enable Miller & Whitney to pay their debts and divide something between them."

In December, 1802, Whitney negotiated the sale of his patent-right with the State of North Carolina. The Legislature laid a tax of *2s. 6d.* upon every saw (some of the gins had forty saws) employed in ginning cotton, to be continued for five years; and after deducting the expenses of collection the returns were faithfully passed over to the patentee. This compensation was regarded by Whitney as more liberal than that received from any other source. About the same time Mr. Goodrich, the agent of the company, entered into a similar negotiation with Tennessee, which State had by this time begun to realize the importance of the invention. The Legislature passed a law laying a tax of $37\frac{1}{2}$ cents per annum on every saw used, for the period of four years. Thus far the prospects were growing favorable to the patentees, when the Legislature of South Carolina unexpectedly annulled the contract which they had made, suspended further payment of the balance, and sued for the refunding of what had been already paid. When Whitney first heard of the transactions of the South Carolina Legislature, he was at Raleigh, where he had just completed a negotiation with the Legislature of North Carolina. In a letter written to Miller at this time, he remarks:

"I am, for my own part, more vexed than alarmed by their extraordinary proceedings. I think it behooves us to be very cautious and very circumspect in our measures, and even in our remarks with regard to it. Be cautious what you say or publish till we meet our enemies in a court of justice, where, if they have any sensibility left, we will make them very much ashamed of their childish conduct."

But that Whitney felt keenly the severities afterward practised against him is evident from the tenor of the remonstrance which he presented to the Legislature:

"The subscriber avers that he has manifested no other than a disposition to fulfil all the stipulations entered into with the State of South Carolina with punctuality and good faith; and he begs leave to observe further, that to have industriously, laboriously, and exclusively devoted many years of the prime of his life to the invention and the improvement of a machine from which the citizens of South Carolina have already realized immense profits, which is worth to them millions, and from which their prosperity must continue to derive the most important profits, and in return to be treated as a felon, a swindler, and a villain, has stung him to the very soul. And when he considers that this cruel persecution is inflicted by the very persons who are enjoying these great benefits, and expressly for the purpose of preventing his ever deriving the least advantage from his own labors, the acuteness of his feelings is altogether inexpressible."

Doubts, it seems, had arisen in the public mind as to the validity of the patent. Great exertions had been made in Georgia, where, it will be remembered, hostilities were first declared against him, to show that his title to the invention was unsound, and that "somebody" in Switzerland had conceived it before him; and that the improved form of the machine with saws, instead of wire teeth, did not come within the patent, having been introduced by one Hodgin Holmes. The popular voice, stimulated by the most sordid methods, was now raised against Whitney throughout all the cotton States. Tennessee followed the example of South Carolina, annulling the contract made with him. And the attempt was made in North Carolina. But a committee of the Legislature, to whom it was referred, reported in Whitney's favor, declaring "that the contract ought to be fulfilled with punctuality and good faith," which resolution was adopted by both Houses. There were also high-minded men in South Carolina who were indignant at the dishonorable measures adopted by their Legislature of 1803; their sentiments impressed the community so favorably with regard to Whitney that, at the session of 1804, the Legislature not only rescinded what the previous one had done, but signified their respect for Whitney by marked commendations.

Miller died on December 7, 1803. In the earlier stages of the enterprise he had indulged high hopes of a great fortune; perpetual disappointments appear to have attended him through life. Whitney was now left alone to contend single-handed against the difficulties which had, for a series of years, almost broken down the spirits of the partners. The light, moreover, which seemed to be breaking, proved but the twilight of prosperity. The favorable issue of Whitney's affairs in South Carolina, and the generous receipts he obtained from his contract with North Carolina, relieved him, however, from the embarrassments under which he had so long groaned, and made him, in some degree, independent. Still, no small portion of the funds thus collected in North and South Carolina was expended in carrying on trials and endless lawsuits in Georgia.

Finally, in the United States Court, held in Georgia, December, 1807, Whitney's patent obtained a most important decision in its favor against a trespasser named Fort. It was on this trial that Judge Johnson gave a most celebrated decision in the following words:

" To support the originality of the invention, the complainants have produced a variety of depositions of witnesses, examined under commission, whose examinations expressly prove the origin, progress, and completion of the machine of Whitney, one of the copartners. Persons who were made privy to his first discovery testify to the several experiments which he made in their presence before he ventured to expose his invention to the scrutiny of the public eye. But it is not necessary to resort to such testimony to maintain this point. The jealousy of the artist to maintain that reputation which his ingenuity has justly acquired, has urged him to unnecessary pains on this subject. There are circumstances in the knowledge of all mankind which prove the originality of this invention more satisfactorily to the mind than the direct testimony of a host of witnesses. The cotton-plant furnished clothing to mankind before the age of Herodotus. The green seed is a species much more productive than the black, and by nature adapted to a much greater variety of climate, but by reason of the strong adherence of the fibre to the seed, without the aid of some more powerful machine for separating it than any formerly known among us, the cultivation of it would never have been made an object. The machine of which Mr. Whitney claims the invention so facilitates the preparation of this species for use that the cultivation of it has suddenly become an object of infinitely greater national importance than that of the other species ever can be. Is it, then, to be imagined that if this machine had been before discovered, the use of it would ever have been lost, or could have been confined to any tract or country left unexplored by commercial enterprise ? But it is unnecessary to remark further upon this subject. A number of years have elapsed since Mr. Whitney took out his patent, and no one has produced or pretended to prove the existence of a machine of similar construction or use.

" With regard to the utility of this discovery the court would deem it a waste of time to dwell long upon this topic. Is there a man who hears us who has not experienced its utility? The whole interior of the Southern States was languishing and its inhabitants emigrating for want of some object to engage their attention and employ their industry, when the invention of this machine at once opened views to them which set the whole country in active motion. From childhood to age it has presented to us a lucrative employment. Our debts have been paid off, our capitals have increased, and our lands trebled themselves in value. We cannot express the weight of the obligation which the country owes to this invention. The extent of it cannot now be seen. Some faint presentiment may be formed from the reflection that cotton is rapidly supplanting wool, flax, silk, and even furs in manufactures, and may one day profitably supply the use of specie in our East India trade. Our sister States also participate in the benefits of this invention, for besides affording the raw material for their manufacturers, the bulkiness and quantity of the article affords a valuable employment for their shipping."

The influence of this decision, however, availed Whitney very little, for the term of his patent had nearly expired. During Miller's life more than sixty suits had been instituted in Georgia, and but a single decision on the merits of the claim was obtained. In prosecution of his troublesome business, Whitney had made six different journeys to Georgia, several of which were accomplished by land at a time when the difficulties of such journeys were exceedingly great. A gentleman who was well acquainted with Whitney's affairs in the South, and sometimes acted as his legal adviser, says that in all his experience in the thorny profession of the law he never saw a case of such perseverance under prosecution. He adds: " Nor do I believe that I ever knew any other man who would have met them with equal coolness and firmness, or who would finally have obtained even the partial success which he did. He always called on me in New York on his way South when going to attend his endless trials and to meet the mischievous contrivances of men who seemed inexhaustible in their resources of evil. Even now, after thirty years, my head aches to recollect his narratives of new trials, fresh disappointments, and accumulated wrongs."

In 1798 Whitney had become deeply impressed with the uncertainty of all his hopes founded upon the cotton-gin, and began to think seriously of devoting himself to some business in which his superior ingenuity, seconded by uncommon industry, would conduct him by a slow but sure road to a competent fortune. It may be considered indicative of solid judgment and a well-balanced mind that he did not, as is so frequently the case with men of inventive genius, become so poisoned with the hopes of vast wealth as to be disqualified for making a reasonable provision for life by the sober earnings of private industry. The enterprise which he selected in accordance with these views was the manufacture of arms for the United States. Through Oliver Wolcott, then Secretary of the Treasury, he obtained a contract for the manufacture of 10,000 stand of arms, 4,000 of which were to be delivered before the last of September of the ensuing year, 1799. Whitney purchased for his works a site called East Rock, near New Haven, now known as Whitneyville, and justly admired for the romantic beauty of its scenery. A water-fall offered the necessary power for the machinery.

Here he began operations with great zeal. His machinery was yet to be built, his material collected, and even his workmen to be taught, and that in a business with which he was imperfectly acquainted.

A severe winter retarded his operations and rendered him incompetent to fulfil the contract. Only 500 instead of 4,000 stands were delivered the first year, and eight years instead of two were found necessary for completing the whole. During the eight years Whitney was occupied in performing this work, he applied himself to business with the most exemplary diligence, rising every morning as soon as it was day, and at night setting everything in order in all parts of the establishment. His genius impressed itself on every part of the factory, extending even to the most common tools, most of which received some peculiar modification which improved them in accuracy or efficiency. His machines for making the several parts of the musket were made to operate with the greatest possible degree of uniformity and precision. The object at which he aimed, and which he fully accomplished, was to make the same parts of different guns, as the locks, for instance, as much like each other as the successive impressions of a copperplate engraving, and it has generally been considered that Whitney greatly improved the way of manufacturing arms and laid his country under permanent obligations by augmenting our facilities for national defence. In 1812 he made a contract to manufacture for the United States 15,000 stand of arms, and in the meantime a similar contract with the State of New York. Several other persons made contracts with the Government at about the same time and attempted the manufacture of muskets. The result of their efforts was a complete failure, and in some instances they expended a considerable fortune in addition to the amount received for their work. In 1822 Calhoun, then Secretary of War, admitted in a conversation with Whitney that the Government was saving $25,000 a year at the public armories alone by his improvements, and it should be remembered that

the utility of Whitney's labors during this part of
his life was not limited to this particular business.

In 1812 Whitney made application to Congress
for the renewal of his patent for the cotton-gin.
In his memorial he presented the history of the
struggles he had been forced to make in defence
of his rights, observing that he had been unable
to obtain any decision on the merits of his claim
until thirteen years of his patent had expired.
He states also that his invention had been a
source of opulence to thousands of the citizens
of the United States; that as a labor-saving
machine it would enable one man to perform the
work of a thousand men, and that it furnished to
the whole family of mankind, at a very cheap
rate, the most essential material for their clothing. Although so great advantages had already
been experienced, and the prospect of future
benefits was so promising, still, many of those
whose interest had been most promoted and the
value of whose property had been most enhanced
by this invention, had obstinately persisted in
refusing to make any compensation to the inventor. From the State in which he had first
made, and where he had first introduced his
machine, and which had derived the most signal
benefits—Georgia—he had received nothing;
and from no State had he received the amount
of half a cent per pound on the cotton cleaned
with his machines in one year. Estimating the
value of the labor of one man at twenty cents a
day, the whole amount which had been received
by him for his invention was not equal to the value

of the labor saved in one hour by his machines then in use in the United States. He continues:

" It is objected that if the patentee succeeds in procuring the renewal of his patent he will be too rich. There is no probability that the patentee, if the term of his patent were extended for twenty years, would ever obtain for his invention one-half as much as many an individual will gain by the use of it. Up to the present time the whole amount of what he had acquired from this source, after deducting his expenses, does not exceed one-half the sum which a single individual has gained by the use of the machine in one year. It is true that considerable sums have been obtained from some of the States where the machine is used, but no small portion of these sums has been expended in prosecuting his claim in a State where nothing has been obtained, and where his machine has been used to the greatest advantage."

Notwithstanding these cogent arguments, the application was rejected by the courts. Some liberal-minded and enlightened men from the cotton districts favored the petition, but a majority of the members from that part of the Union were warmly opposed to granting it. In a letter to Robert Fulton, Whitney says:

" The difficulties with which I have to contend have originated, principally, in the want of a disposition in mankind to do justice. My invention was new and distinct from every other; it stood alone. It was not interwoven with anything before known; and it can seldom happen that an invention or improvement is so strongly marked and can be so clearly and specifically identified; and I have always believed that I should have no difficulty in causing my right to be respected, if it had been less valuable, and been used only by a small portion of the community. But the use of this machine being immensely profitable to almost every planter in the cotton districts, all were interested in trespassing upon the patent-right, and each kept the other in countenance. Demagogues made themselves popular by mis-representations and unfounded clamors, both against the right and against the law made for its protection. Hence there arose associations and combinations to oppose both. At one time, but few men in Georgia dared to come into court and testify to the most simple facts within their knowledge, relative to the use of the machine. In one instance I had great difficulty in proving that the machine had been used in Georgia, although at the same moment there were three separate sets of this machinery in motion within fifty yards of the building in which the court sat, and all so near that the rattling of the wheels was distinctly heard on the steps of the court-house."

Such perseverance, patience, and uncommon skill were not, however, to go wholly unre-warded. Whitney's factory of arms in New Haven made money for him, and the Southern States were not all guilty of ingratitude. More-over, in his private life he was extremely fortu-

7

nate. In January, 1817, he married Henrietta
Edwards, the youngest daughter of Judge Pier-
pont Edwards, of Connecticut. A son and three
daughters contributed to the sunshine of the
close of a somewhat stormy and eventful life.
His last years were his happiest. He found
prosperity and honor in New Haven, where he
died on January 8, 1825, after a tedious illness.

In person Whitney was of more than usual
height, with much dignity of manner and an
open, pleasant face. Among his particular
friends no man was more esteemed. Some of
the earliest of his intimate associates were among
the latest. His sense of honor was high, and his
feeling of resentment and indignation under injustice correspondingly strong. He could, however, be cool when his opponents were hot, and
his strong sense of the injuries he had suffered
did not impair the natural serenity of his temper.
The value of his famous invention has so steadily
grown that its money importance to this country
can scarcely be estimated in figures. His tomb
in New Haven is after a model of that of Scipio,
at Rome, and bears the following inscription:

ELI WHITNEY,

The Inventor of the Cotton-Gin.

OF USEFUL SCIENCE AND ARTS, THE EFFICIENT PATRON
AND IMPROVER.

IN THE SOCIAL RELATIONS OF LIFE, A MODEL OF EXCEL-
LENCE.

WHILE PRIVATE AFFECTION WEEPS AT HIS TOMB, HIS
COUNTRY HONORS HIS MEMORY.

BORN DEC. 8, 1765. DIED JAN. 8, 1825.

IV.

ELIAS HOWE.

In looking over the history of great inventions it is remarkable how uniformly those discoveries that helped mankind most have been derided, abused, and opposed by the very classes which in the end they were destined to bless. Nearly every great invention has had literally to be forced into popular acceptance. The bowmen of the Middle Ages resisted the introduction of the musket; the sedan-chair carriers would not allow hackney carriages to be used; the stage-coach lines attempted by all possible devices to block the advance of the railway. When, in 1707, Dr. Papin showed his first rude conception of a steamboat, it was seized by the boatmen, who feared that it would deprive them of a living. Kay was mobbed in Lancashire when he tried to introduce his fly-shuttle; Hargreaves had his spinning-frame destroyed by a Blackburn mob; Crampton had to hide his spinning-mule in a lumber-room for fear of a similar fate; Arkwright, the inventor of the spinning-frame, was de-nounced as the enemy of the working-classes and his mill destroyed; Jacquard narrowly es-caped being thrown into the river Rhone by a crowd of furious weavers when his new loom

Elias Howe.

was first put into operation ; Cartwright had to abandon his power-loom for years because of the bitter animosity of the weavers toward it. Riots were organized in Nottingham against the use of the stocking-loom.

It is not therefore surprising that the greatest labor-saving machine of domestic life, the sewing-machine, should have been received with anything but thanks. Howe was abused, ridiculed, and denounced as the enemy of man, and especially of poor sewing-women, the very class whose toil he has done so much to lighten. Curses instead of blessings were showered upon him during the first years that followed the successful working of his wonderful machine. Fortunately for the inventor, the age of persecution had almost passed, and Howe lived to receive the rewards he so fully deserved.

Elias Howe, Jr., was born in Spencer, Mass., in 1819. His father was a farmer and miller, and the eight children of the family, as was common with all poor people of the time, were early taught to do light work of one kind or another. When Elias was six years old he was set with his brothers and sisters at sticking wire teeth through the leather straps used for cotton-cards. When older he helped his father in the mill, and in summer picked up a little book knowledge at the district school. As a boy he was frail in constitution, and he was slightly lame. When eleven years old he attempted farm labor for a neighbor, but was not strong enough for it and returned to his father's mill, where he remained until he was sixteen. It was here that he first began to like machinery. A friend who had visited Lowell gave him such an account of that bustling city and its big mills that young Howe, becoming dissatisfied, obtained his father's consent to leave, and found employment in one of the Lowell cotton-mills. The financial crash of 1837 stopped the looms, and Howe obtained a place in a Cambridge machine-shop in which his cousin, Nathaniel P. Banks, afterward Governor of Massachusetts, also worked. Howe's first job happened to be upon a new hemp-carding machine of Treadwell.

At the age of twenty-one Howe married and moved to Boston, finding employment in the machine-shop of Ari Davis. He is described as being a capital workman, more full of resources than of plodding industry, however, and rather apt to spend more time in suggesting a better way of doing a job than in following instructions. With such a disposition, and inasmuch as his suggestions were not considered of value, he had rather a hard time of it. Three children were born to the young couple. As Howe's earnings were slight and his health none of the best, his wife tried to add to the family income, and at evening, when Howe lay exhausted upon the bed after his day's work, the young mother patiently sewed. Her toil was to some purpose. With his natural bent for mechanics, Howe could not be a silent witness of this incessant and poorly paid labor without becoming interested in affording aid. Moreover, he was constantly employed upon new spinning and weaving machines for doing work that for thousands of years had been done painfully and slowly by hand. The possibility of sewing by machinery had often been spoken of before that day, but the problem seemed to present insuperable difficulties.

Elias Howe had, as we know, peculiar fitness for such work. He had seen much of inventors and inventions, and knew something of the dangers and disappointments in store for him. In the intervals between important jobs at the shop he nursed the idea of a sewing-machine, keeping his own counsel. In his first rude attempt it appeared to him that machine-sewing could only be accomplished with very coarse thread or string ; fine thread would not stand the strain. For his first machine he made a needle pointed at both ends, with an eye in the middle ; it was arranged to work up and down, carrying the thread through at each thrust. It was only after more than a year's work upon this device that he decided it would not do. This first attempt was a sort of imitation of sewing by hand, the machine following more or less the movements of the hand. Finally, after repeated failures, it became plain to him that something radically different was needed, and that there must be another stitch, and perhaps another needle or half a dozen needles, in such a machine. He then conceived the idea of using two threads, and making the stitch by means of a shuttle and a curved needle with the eye near the point. This was the real solution of the problem. In

October, 1844, he made a rough model of his first sewing-machine, all of wood and wire, and found that it would actually sew.

In one of the earliest accounts of the invention it is thus described: "He used a needle and a shuttle of novel construction, and combined them with holding surfaces, feed mechanism, and other devices as they had never before been brought together in one machine. . . . One of the principal features of Mr. Howe's invention is the combination of a grooved needle having an eye near its point, and vibrating in the direction of its length, with a side-pointed shuttle for effecting a locked stitch, and forming with the threads, one on each side of the cloth, a firm and lasting seam not easily ripped."

Meanwhile Howe had given up work as a machinist and had moved to his father's house in Cambridge, where the elder Howe had a shop for the cutting of palm-leaf used in the manufacture of hats. Here Elias and his little family lived, and in the garret the inventor put up a lathe upon which he made the parts of his sewing-machine. To provide for his family he did such odd jobs as he could find; but it was hard work to get bread, to say nothing of butter, and to make matters worse his father lost his shop by fire. Elias knew that his sewing-machine would work, but he had no money wherewith to buy the materials for a machine of steel and iron, and without such a machine he could not hope to interest capital in it. He needed at least $500 with which to prove the value of his great invention.

Fortune threw in his way a coal and wood dealer of Cambridge, named Fisher, who had some money. Fisher liked the invention and agreed to board Howe and his family, to give Howe a workshop in his house, and to advance the $500 necessary for the construction of a first machine. In return he was to become a half owner in the patent should Howe succeed in obtaining one. In December, 1844, Howe accordingly moved into Fisher's house, and here the new marvel was brought into the world. All that winter Howe worked over his device in Fisher's garret, making many changes as unforeseen difficulties arose. He worked all day, and sometimes nearly all night, succeeding by April, 1845, in sewing a seam four yards long with his machine. By the middle of May the machine was completed, and in July Howe sewed with it the seams of two woollen suits, one for himself and the other for Fisher; the sewing was so well done that it promised to outlast the cloth. For many years this machine was exhibited in a shop in New York. It showed how completely, at really the first attempt, Howe had mastered the enormous difficulties in his way. Its chief features are those upon which were founded all the sewing-machines that followed.

Late in 1845 Howe obtained his first patent and began to take means to introduce his sewing-machine to the public. He first offered it to the tailors of Boston, who admitted its usefulness, but assured him that it would never be adopted, as it would ruin their trade. Other

efforts were equally unsuccessful; the more perfectly the machine did its work, the more obsti-
nate and determined seemed to be the resistance
to it.   Everyone admitted and praised the ingenuity of the invention, but no one would invest a
dollar in it.   Fisher became disheartened and
withdrew from the partnership, and Howe and
his family moved back into his father's house.

For a time the poor inventor abandoned his
machine and obtained a place as engineer on a
railway, driving a locomotive, until his health
entirely broke down.   Forced to turn again to
his beloved sewing-machine for want of anything
better to do, Howe decided to send his brother
Amasa to England with a machine.   Amasa
reached London in October, 1846, and met a certain William Thomas, to whom he explained the
invention.   Thomas was much impressed with
its possibilities and offered $1,250 for the ma-
chine and also to engage Elias Howe at $15 a
week if he would enter his business of umbrella
and corset maker.   This was at least a livelihood
to the latter, and he sailed for England, where
for the next eight months he worked for Thomas,
whom he found an uncommonly hard master.
He was indeed so harshly treated that, although
his wife and three children had arrived in London, he threw up his situation.   For a time his
condition was a piteous one.   He was in a strange
country, without friends or money.   For days at
a time the little family were without more than
crusts to live upon.

Believing that he could struggle along better

alone, Howe sent his family home with the first few dollars that he could obtain from the other side and remained in London. There were certain things which caused him to hope for better times ahead. But such hopes were delusive, it seems, and after some months of hardship he followed his family to this country, pawning his model and his patent papers in order to obtain the necessary money for the passage. As he landed in New York with less than a dollar in his pocket, he received news that his wife was dying of consumption in Cambridge. He had no money for travelling by rail, and he was too feeble to attempt the journey on foot. It took him some days to obtain the money for his fare to Boston, but he arrived in time to be present at the death-bed of his wife. Before he could recover from this blow he had news that the ship by which he had sent home the few household goods still remaining to him had gone to the bottom.

This was poor Howe's darkest hour. Others had seen the value of the sewing-machine, and during his absence in England several imitations of it had been made and sold to great advantage by unscrupulous mechanics, who had paid no attention to the rights of the inventor. Such machines were already spoken of as wonders by the newspapers, and were beginning to be used in several industries. Howe's patent was so strong that it was not difficult to find money to defend it, once the practical value of the invention had been well established, and in August,

1850, he began several suits to make his rights clear. At the same time he moved to New York, where he began in a small way to manufacture machines in partnership with a business man named Bliss, who undertook to sell them.

It was not until Howe's rights to the invention had been fully established, which was done by the decision of Judge Sprague, in 1854, that the real value of the sewing-machine as a money-making venture began to be apparent; and even then its great importance was so little realized, even by Bliss, who was in the business and died in 1855, that Howe was enabled to buy the interest of his heirs for a small sum. It was during these efforts to introduce the sewing-machine that occurred what were known as the sewing-machine riots—disturbances of no special importance, however—fomented by labor leaders in the New York shops in which cheap clothing was manufactured. Howe's sewing-machine was denounced as a menace to the thousands of men and women who worked in these shops, and in several establishments the first Howe machines introduced were so injured by mischievous persons as to retard the success of the experiment for nearly a year. Failing to stop their introduction by such means a public demonstration against them was organized and for a time threatened such serious trouble that some of the large shops gave up the use of the machine; but in small establishments employing but a few workmen they continued to be used and were soon found to be so indispensable that all opposition faded away.

The patent suits forced upon Howe by a number of infringers were costly drains upon the inventor, but in the end all other manufacturers were compelled to pay tribute to him, and in six years his royalties grew from $300 to more than $200,000 a year. In 1863 his royalties were estimated at $4,000 a day. At the Paris Exposition of 1867 he was awarded a gold medal and the ribbon of the Legion of Honor.

Howe's health, never strong, was so thoroughly broken by the years of struggle and hardship he met with while trying to introduce his machine that he never completely recovered. If honors and money were any comfort to him, his last years must have been happy ones, for his invention made him famous, and he had been enough of a workingman to recognize the blessing he had conferred upon millions of women released from the slavery of the needle; he had answered Hood's "Song of the Shirt." He died on October 3, 1867, at his home in Brooklyn, N. Y.

Those who knew Howe personally speak of him as rather a handsome man, with a head somewhat like Franklin's and a reserved, quiet manner. His bitter struggle against poverty and disease left its impress upon him even to the last. One trait frequently mentioned was his readiness to find good points in the thousand and one variations and sometimes improvements upon his invention. During the years 1858-67, when he died, there were recorded nearly three hundred patents affecting the sewing-machine, taken out by other inventors. Howe was always ready to help along such improvements by advice and often by money. He fought sturdily for his rights, but once those conceded he was a generous rival.

V.

SAMUEL F. B. MORSE.

Samuel Finley Breese Morse was the eldest son of the Rev. Jedediah Morse, an eminent New England divine. The Rev. Samuel Finley, D.D., second president of the College of New

Birthplace of S. F. B. Morse, Built 1775.

Jersey, Princeton, was his maternal great-grand-father, after whom he was named. Breese was the maiden name of his mother. The famous inventor of the telegraph was born at the foot of Breed's Hill, Charlestown, Mass., April 27, 1791.

Dr. Belknap, of Boston, writing to Postmaster-General Hazard, New York, says:

"Congratulate the Monmouth judge (Mr. Breese, the grandfather) on the birth of a grandson. Next Sunday he is to be loaded with names, not quite so many as the Spanish ambassador who signed the treaty of peace of 1783, but only four. As to the child, I saw him asleep, so can say nothing of his eye, or his genius peeping through it. He may have the sagacity of a Jewish rabbi, or the profundity of a Calvin, or the sublimity of a Homer for aught I know, but time will bring forth all things."

Jedediah Morse studied theology under the Rev. Dr. Jonathan Edwards. Before he began preaching, and while teaching school in New Haven, he began his "American Geography," which was afterward indentified with his name. He began his ministry at Norwich, whence he was called back to be tutor in Yale. His health was inadequate to the work and he went to Georgia, returning to Charlestown, Mass., as pastor of the First Congregational Church, on the day that Washington was inaugurated as President in New York, April 30, 1789. Dr. Eliot, speaking of Jedediah Morse, said: "What an astonishing impetus that man has!" President Dwight said: "He is as full of resources as an egg is of meat." Daniel Webster spoke of him as "always thinking, always writing, always talking, always acting."

Morse's mother, Elizabeth Anne Breese, came of good Scotch-Irish stock. She was married to

Jédediah Morse in 1789, and was noted as a calm, judicious, and thinking woman, with a will of her own. When the child, Samuel F. B. Morse, was four years old he was sent to school to an old lady within a few hundred yards of the parsonage. She was an invalid, unable to leave her chair, and

S. F. B. Morse.

governed her unruly flock with a long rattan which reached across the small room in which it was gathered. One of her punishments was pinning the culprit to her own dress, and Morse remarks that his first attempts at drawing were discouraged in this fashion. Perhaps the fact that he selected the old lady's face as a model had something to do with it. At the age of seven he

8

was sent to school at Andover, where he was fitted for entering Phillips Academy, and prepared here for Yale, joining the class of 1807. When he was thirteen years old, at Andover, he wrote a sketch of Demosthenes and sent it to his father, by whom it was preserved as a mark of the learning and taste of the child. Dr. Timothy Dwight was then president of Yale and a warm friend of the elder Morse. Finley Morse, as he was then known, received therefore the deep personal interest of Dr. Dwight. Jeremiah Day was professor of natural philosophy in Yale College, and under his instruction Morse began the study of electricity, receiving perhaps those impressions that were destined to produce so great an influence upon him and, through him, upon this century. Professor Day was then young and ardent in the pursuit of science, kindling readily the enthusiasm of his students. He afterward became president of the college. There was at the same time in the faculty Benjamin Silliman, who was professor of chemistry, and near whom Morse resided for several years. Years afterward the testimony of Professors Day and Silliman was given in court, when it was important, in the defence of his claim to priority in the invention of the telegraph. Through them Morse was able to show that he was early interested in the study of chemistry and electricity. During this litigation Morse did not know that there were scores of letters, written by him as a young student to his father, among the papers of Dr Jedediah Morse, that would have shown conclusively his interest and aptitude in these studies. The papers were brought to light when the life of Morse by Prime came to be written.

The first part of Morse's life was devoted to art. At a very early age he showed his taste in this direction, and at the age of fifteen painted a fairly good picture in water colors of a room in his father's house, with his parents, himself, and two brothers around a table. This picture used to hang in his home in New York by the side of his last painting. From that time his desire to become an artist haunted him through his collegiate life. In February, 1811, he painted a picture, now in the office of the mayor of Charlestown, Mass., depicting the landing of the Pilgrims at Plymouth, which, with a landscape painted at about the same time, decided his father, by the advice of Stuart, to permit him to visit Europe with Washington Allston. He bore letters to West and to Copley, from both of whom he received the kindest attention and encouragement.

As a test for his fitness for a place as student in the Royal Academy, Morse made a drawing from a small cast of the Farnese Hercules. He took this to West, who examined the drawing carefully and handed it back, saying: "Very well, sir, very well; go on and finish it." "It is finished," said the expectant student. "Oh, no," said the president. "Look here, and here, and here," pointing out many unfinished places which had escaped the eye of the young artist. Morse quickly observed the defects, spent a week in further perfecting his drawing, and then took it to West, confident that it was above criticism. The venerable president of the Academy bestowed more praise than before and, with a pleasant smile, handed it back to Morse, saying: "Very well, indeed, sir. Go on and finish it." "Is it not finished?" inquired the almost discouraged student. "See," said West, "you have not marked that muscle, nor the articulation of the finger-joints." Three days more were spent upon the drawing, when it was taken back to the implacable critic. "Very clever, indeed," said West; "very clever. Now go on and finish it." "I cannot finish it," Morse replied, when the old man, patting him on the shoulder, said: "Well, I have tried you long enough. Now, sir, you have learned more by this drawing than you would have accomplished in double the time by a dozen half-finished beginnings. It is not many drawings, but the character of one which makes a thorough draughtsman. Finish one picture, sir, and you are a painter."

Morse heeded this advice. He went to work with Allston, and encouraged by the veteran, Copley, he began upon a large picture for exhibition in the Royal Academy, choosing as his subject "The Dying Hercules." He modelled his figure in clay, as the best of the old painters did. It was his first attempt in the sculptor's art. The cast was made in plaster and taken to West, who was delighted with it. This model contended for the prize of a gold medal offered by the Society of Arts for the best original cast of a single figure, and won it. In the large room of the London Adelphi, in the presence of the British nobility, foreign ambassadors, and distinguished strangers, the Duke of Norfolk publicly presented the medal to Morse on May 13, 1813. At the same time the painting from this model, then on exhibition at the Royal Academy, received great praise from the critics, who placed " The Dying Hercules " among the first twelve pictures in a collection of almost two thousand.

This was an extraordinary success for so young a man, and Morse determined to try for the highest prize offered by the Royal Academy for the best historical composition, the decision to be made in 1815. For that purpose he produced his " Judgment of Jupiter " in July of that year. West assured him that it would take the prize, but Morse was unable to comply with the rules of the Academy, which required the victor to receive the medal in person. His father had summoned him home. West urged the Academy to make an exception in his case, but it could not be done, and the young painter had to be contented with his assurances that he would certainly have won the prize (a gold medal and $250) had he remained.

West was always kind to Americans, and Morse was a favorite with him. One day, when the venerable painter was at work upon his great picture, " Christ Rejected," after carefully examining Morse's hands and noting their beauty, he said : " Let me tie you with this cord and take that place while I paint in the hands of the Saviour." This was done, and when he released the young artist, he said to him : " You may now say, if you please, that you had a hand in this picture." A number of noted English artists—Turner, Northcote, Sir James Lawrence, Flaxman—and literary men—Coleridge, Wordsworth, Rogers, and Crabbe among them—were attracted by young Morse's proficiency and pleasant manners, and when in August, 1815, he packed his picture, " The Judgment of Jupiter," and sailed for home, he bore with him the good wishes of some of England's most distinguished men.

When Morse reached Boston, although but twenty-four years old, he found that fame had preceded him. His prestige was such that he set up his easel with high hopes and fair prospects for the future, both destined soon to be dispelled. The taste of America had not risen to the appreciation of historical pictures. His original compositions and his excellent copies of the masterpieces of the Old World excited the admiration of cultured people, but no orders were given for them. He left Boston almost penniless after having waited for months for patronage, and determined to try to earn his bread by painting the portraits of people in the rural districts of New England, where his father's name was a household word. During the autumn of 1816 and the winter of 1816–1817 he visited several towns in New Hampshire and Vermont, painting portraits in Walpole, Hanover, Windsor, Portsmouth, and Concord. He received the modest sum of $15 for each portrait. From Concord, N. H., he writes to his parents : " I am still here (August 16th) and am passing my time very agreeably. I have painted five portraits at $15 each, and have two more engaged and many talked of. I think I shall get along well. I believe I could make an independent fortune in a few years if I devoted myself exclusively to portraits, so great is the desire for good portraits in the different country towns." He doubtless was candid when he wrote that he was "passing his time in Concord very agreeably," for it was here that he met Lucretia P. Walker, who was accounted the most beautiful and accomplished young lady of the town, whom Morse subsequently married. She was a young woman of great personal loveliness and rare good sense. The young artist was attracted by her beauty, her sweetness of temper, and high intellectual qualities. All the letters that she wrote to him before and after their marriage he carefully preserved, and these are witnesses to her intelligence, education, tenderness of feeling, and admirable fitness to be the wife of such a man. Gradually Morse's portraits became so much in demand that he was enabled to increase his price to $60, and as he painted four a week upon the average, and received a good deal of money during a tour in the South, he was enabled to return to New England in 1818 with $3,000, and to marry Miss Walker on October 6th of that year.

The first years of Morse's married life were passed in Charleston, S. C., after which he returned to New England, and having laid by some little capital, he took up again what he deemed to be his real vocation—the painting of great historical pictures. His first venture in this direction was an exhibition picture of the House of Representatives at Washington. As a business venture it was disastrous, and resulted in the loss of eighteen months of precious time. It was finally sold to an Englishman. Then began Morse's life in New York. Through the influence of Isaac Lawrence he obtained a commission from the city authorities of New York to paint a full-length portrait of Lafayette, who was then in this country. He had just completed his study from life in Washington in February, 1825, when he received the news of the death of his wife. A little more than a year afterward both his father and mother died. Thenceforward his children and art absorbed his affections.

He was an artist, heart and soul, and his professional brethren soon had good reason to be grateful to him. The American Academy of Fine Arts, then under the presidency of Colonel John Trumbull, was in a languishing state and of little use to artists. The most advanced of its members felt the need of relief, and a few of them met at Morse's rooms to discuss their troubles. At that meeting Morse proposed the formation of a new society of artists, and at a meeting held at the New York Historical Society's rooms the "New York Drawing Association" was organized, with Morse as its president. Trumbull endeavored to compel the new society to profess allegiance to the academy, but Morse protested, and thanks to his advice, on January

18, 1826, a new art association was organized
under the name of the "National Academy of
Design." Morse was its first president, and for
sixteen years he was annually elected to that
office. The friends of the old academy were
wrathful and assailed the new association. A
war of words, in which Morse acted as the cham-

Under Side of a Modern Switchboard, showing 2,000 Wires.

pion of the new society, was waged until victory
was conceded to the reformers. Thus Morse
inaugurated a new era in the history of the fine
arts in this country. He wrote, talked, lectured
incessantly for the advancement of art and the
Academy of Design.

In 1829 Morse made a second visit to Europe,
where he was warmly welcomed and honored by

the Royal Academy. During three years or
more he lived in continental cities, studying the
Louvre in Paris and making of the famous gal-
lery an exhibition picture which contained about
fifty miniatures of the works in that collection.
In November, 1832, he was back again in New
York, with high hopes as to his future. Allston,
writing to Dunlap in 1834, said: "I rejoice to
hear your report of Morse's advance in his art.
I know what is in him perhaps better than anyone else. If he will only bring out all that is
there he will show parts that many now do not
dream of."

For several years the thoughts of the artist
Morse had been busy with a matter wholly outside of his chosen domain. Some lectures on
electro-magnetism by his intimate friend, Judge
Freeman Dana, given at the Athenæum while
Morse was also lecturing there on the fine arts,
had greatly interested him in the subject, and he
learned much in conversation with Dana. While
on his second visit to Europe Morse made himself acquainted with the labors of scientific men
in their endeavors to communicate intelligence
between far-distant places by means of electro-
magnetism, and he saw an electro-magnet signalling instrument in operation. He knew that so
early as 1649 a Jesuit priest had prophesied an
electric telegraph, and that for half a century or
more students had partially succeeded in attempts of this kind. But no practical telegraph
had yet been invented. In 1774 Le Sage made
an electro-signalling instrument with twenty-four

wires, one for each letter of the alphabet. In 1825 Sturgeon invented an electro-magnet. In 1830 Professor Henry increased the magnetic force that Morse afterward used.

On board the ship Sully, in which Morse sailed from Havre to New York, in the autumn of 1832, the recent discovery in France of the means of obtaining an electric spark from a magnet was a favorite topic of conversation among the passengers, and it was during the voyage that Morse conceived the idea of an electro-magnetic and chemical recording telegraph. Before he reached New York he had made drawings and specifications of his conception, which he exhibited to his fellow passengers. Few great inventions that have made their authors immortal were so completely grasped at inception as this. Morse was accustomed to keep small note-books in which to make records of his work, and scores of these books are still in existence. As he sat upon the deck of the Sully, one night after dinner, he drew from his pocket one of these books and began to make marks to represent letters and figures to be produced by electricity at a distance. The mechanism by which the results were to be reached was wrought out by slow and laborious thought, but the vision as a whole was clear. The current of electricity passed instantaneously to any distance along a wire, but the current being interrupted, a spark appeared. This spark represented one sign; its absence another; the time of its absence still another. Here are three signs to be combined into the representation of figures or letters. They can be made to form an alphabet. Words may thus be indicated. A telegraph, an instrument to record at a distance, will result. Contients shall be crossed. This great and wide sea shall be no barrier. " If it will go ten miles without stopping," he said, " I can make it go around the globe."

He worked incessantly all that next day and could not sleep at night in his berth. In a few days he submitted some rough drafts of his invention to William C. Rives, of Virginia, who was returning from Paris, where he had been minister of the United States. Mr. Rives suggested various difficulties, over which Morse spent several sleepless nights, announcing in the morning at breakfast-table the new devices by which he proposed to accomplish the task before him. He exhibited a drawing of the instrument which he said would do the work, and so completely had he mastered all the details that five years afterward, when a model of this instrument was constructed, it was instantly recognized as the one he had devised and drawn in his sketch-book and exhibited to his fellow passengers on the ship. In view of subsequent claims made by a fellow passenger to the honor of having suggested the telegraph, these details are interesting and important.

Circumstances delayed the construction of a recording telegraph by Morse, but the subject slumbered in his mind. During his absence abroad he had been elected professor of the literature of the arts of design, in the University of the City of New York, and this work occupied his attention for some time. Three years afterward, in November, 1835, he completed a rude telegraph instrument—the first recording

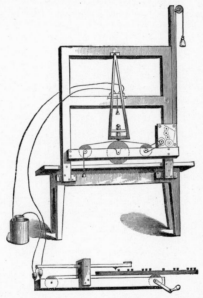

The First Telegraphic Instrument, as Exhibited in 1837 by Morse.

apparatus; but it embodied the mechanical principle now in use the world over. His whole plan was not completed until July, 1837, when by means of two instruments he was able to communicate from as well as to a distant point. In September hundreds of people saw the new instrument in operation at the university, most of whom looked upon it as a scientific toy constructed by an unfortunate dreamer. The following year the invention was sufficiently perfected to enable Morse to direct the attention of Congress to it and ask its aid in the construction of an experimental line between Washington and Baltimore.

Late in the long session of 1838 he appeared before that body with his instrument. Before leaving New York with it he had invited a few friends to see it work. Now began in the life of Morse a period of years during which his whole time was devoted to convincing the world, first, that his electric telegraph would really communicate messages, and, secondly, that if it worked at all, it was of great practical value. Strange to say that this required any argument at all. But that in those days it did may be inferred from the fact that Morse could then find no help far or near. His invention was regarded as interesting, but of no importance either scientifically or commercially. In Washington, where he first went, he found so little encouragement that he went to Europe with the hope of drawing the attention of foreign governments to the advantages, and of securing patents for the invention; he had filed a caveat at the Patent Office in this country. His mission was a failure. England refused him a patent, and France gave him only a useless paper which assured for him no special privileges. He returned home disappointed but not discouraged, and waited four years longer before he again attempted to interest Congress in his invention.

This extraordinary struggle lasted twelve years, during which, with his mind absorbed in one idea and yet almost wholly dependent for bread upon his profession as an artist, it was im-

The Modern Morse Telegraph.

possible to pursue art with the enthusiasm and industry essential to success. His situation was forlorn in the extreme. The father of three little children, now motherless, his pecuniary means exhausted by his residence in Europe, and unable to pursue art without sacrificing his invention, he was at his wits' ends. He had visions of usefulness by the invention of a telegraph that should bring the continents of the earth into intercourse. He was poor and knew that wealth as well as fame was within his reach. He had long received assistance from his father and brothers when his profession did not supply the needed means of support for himself and family; but it seemed like robbery to take the money of others for experiments, the success of which he could not expect them to believe in until he could give practical evidence that the instrument would do the work proposed. It was the old story of genius contending with poverty. His brothers comforted, encouraged, and cheered him. In the house of his brother Richard he found a home and the tender care that he required. Sidney, the other brother, also helped him. On the corner of Nassau and Beekman Streets, now the site of the handsome Morse Building, his brothers erected a building where were the offices of the newspaper of which they were the editors and proprietors. In the fifth story of this building a room was assigned to him which was for several years his studio, bedroom, parlor, kitchen, and workshop. On one side of the room stood a little cot on which he slept in the brief hours which he allowed himself for repose. On the other side stood his lathe with which the inventor turned the brass apparatus necessary in the construction of his instruments. He had, with his own hands, first whittled the model; then he made the moulds for the castings. Here were brought to him, day by day, crackers and the simplest food, by which, with tea prepared by himself, he sustained life while he toiled incessantly to give being to the idea that possessed him.

Before leaving for Europe he had suffered a great disappointment as an artist. The government had offered to American artists, to be selected by a committee of Congress, commissions to paint pictures for the panels in the rotunda of the Capitol. Morse was anxious to be employed upon one or more of them. He was the president of the National Academy of Design, and there was an eminent fitness in calling him to this national work. Allston urged the appoint-

Morse Making his own Instrument.

(From Prime's Life of Morse.)

ment of Morse. John Quincy Adams, then a member of the House and on the committee to whom this subject was referred, submitted a resolution in the House that foreign artists be allowed to compete for these commissions, and in support alleged that there were no American artists competent to execute the paintings. This gave great and just offence to the artists and the public. A severe reply to Adams appeared in the New York *Evening Post*. It was written by James Fenimore Cooper, but it was attributed to Morse, whose pen was well known to be skilful, and in consequence his name was rejected by the committee. He never recovered fully from the effects of that blow. Forty years afterward he could not speak of it without emotion. He had consecrated years of his life to the preparation for just such work.

It was well for him and for his country and the world that the artist in Morse was disappointed. From painter he became inventor, and from that time until the world acknowledged the greatness and importance of his invention he turned not back. His appointment as professor in the City University entitled him to certain rooms in the University Building looking out upon Washington Square, and here the first working models of the telegraph were brought into existence.

" There," he says, " I immediately commenced, with very limited means, to experiment upon my invention. My first instrument was made up of an old picture or canvas frame fas-

tened to a table; the wheels of an old wooden
clock, moved by a weight to carry the paper
forward; three wooden drums, upon one of
which the paper was wound and passed over
the other two; a wooden pendulum suspended
to the top piece of the picture or stretching
frame and vibrating across the paper as it
passes over the centre wooden drum; a pencil

Train Telegraph—the message transmitted by induction from the moving train to
the single wire.

at the lower end of the pendulum, in contact
with the paper; an electro-magnet fastened to a
shelf across the picture or stretching frame, opposite to an armature made fast to the pendulum; a type rule and type for breaking the
circuit, resting on an endless band, composed of
carpet-binding, which passed over two wooden
rollers moved by a wooden crank.

"Up to the autumn of 1837 my telegraphic
apparatus existed in so rude a form that I felt a

reluctance to have it seen. My means were very limited—so limited as to preclude the possibility of constructing an apparatus of such mechanical

Interior of a Car on the Lehigh Valley Railroad, showing the Method of Operating the Train Telegraph.

finish as to warrant my success in venturing upon its public exhibition. I had no wish to expose to ridicule the representative of so many hours of laborious thought. Prior to the summer of 1837, at which time Mr. Alfred Vail's attention became attracted to my telegraph, I depended upon my pencil for subsistence. Indeed, so straitened were my circumstances that, in order to save time to carry out my invention and to economize my scanty means, I had for many months lodged and eaten in my studio, procuring my food in small quantities from some grocery and preparing it myself. To conceal from my friends the stinted manner in which I lived, I was in the habit of bringing my food to my room in the evenings, and this was my mode of life for many years."

Before the telegraph was actually tried and practised the cumbersome piano-key board devised by Morse in his first experiments was done away with and the simple device of a single key, with which we are all familiar, was adopted. Meantime Morse was practically abandoning art. His friends among the profession had subscribed $3,000 in order to enable him to paint the picture he had in mind when he applied for the government work at Washington, " The Signing of the First Compact on Board the Mayflower," and he undertook the commission in 1838, only to give it up in 1841 and to return to the subscribers the amount paid with interest.

While Morse had been in Paris, in 1839, he had heard of Daguerre, who had discovered the method of fixing the image of the camera, which feat was then creating a great sensation among scientific men. Professor Morse was anxious to see the results of this discovery before leaving Paris, and the American consul, Robert Walsh, arranged an interview between the two inventors. Daguerre promised to send to Morse a copy of the descriptive publication which he intended to make so soon as a pension he expected from the French Government for the disclosure of his discovery should be secured. He kept his

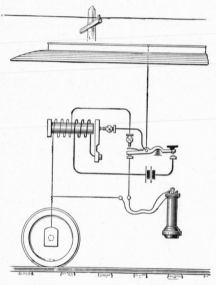

Diagram showing the Method of Telegraphing from a Moving Train by Induction.

promise, and Morse was probably the first recipient of the pamphlet in this country. From the drawings it contained he constructed the first photographic apparatus made in the United States, and from a back window in the University Building he obtained a good representation of the tower of the Church of the Messiah on Broadway. This possesses an historical interest as being the first photograph in America. It was on a plate the size of a playing-card. With Professor J. W. Draper, in a studio built on the roof of the University, he succeeded in taking likenesses of the living human face. His subjects were compelled to sit fifteen minutes in the bright sunlight, with their eyes closed, of course. Professor Draper shortened the process and was the first to take portraits with the eyes open.

At the session of Congress of 1842–1843 Morse again appeared with his telegraph, and on February 21, 1843, John P. Kennedy, of Maryland, moved that a bill appropriating $30,000, to be expended, under the direction of the Secretary of the Treasury, in a series of experiments for testing the merits of the telegraph, should be considered. The proposal met with ridicule. Johnson, of Tennessee, moved, as an amendment, that one-half should be given to a lecturer on mesmerism, then in Washington, to try mesmeric experiments under the direction of the Secretary of the Treasury; and Mr. Houston said that Millerism ought to be included in the benefits of the appropriation. After the indulgence of much cheap wit, Mr. Mason, of Ohio, protested against such frivolity as injurious to the character of the House and asked the chair to rule the amendments out of order. The chair (John White, of Kentucky) ruled the amendments in order because "it would require a scientific analysis to determine how far the magnetism of the mesmerism was analogous to that to be employed in telegraphy." This wit was applauded by peals of laughter, but the amendment was voted down and the bill passed the House on February 23d by the close vote of 89 to 83. In the Senate the bill met with neither sneers nor opposition, but its progress was discouragingly slow. At twilight on the last evening of the session (March 3, 1842) there were one hundred and nineteen bills before it. It seemed impossible for it to be reached in regular course before the hour of adjournment should arrive, and Morse, who had anxiously watched the dreary course of business all day from the gallery of the Senate chamber, went with a sad heart to his hotel and prepared to leave for New York at an early hour the next morning. His cup of disappointment seemed to be about full. With the exception of Alfred Vail, a young student in the University, through whose influence some money had been subscribed in return for a one-fourth interest in the invention, and of Professor L. D. Gale, who had shown much interest in the work and was also a partner in the enterprise, Morse knew of no one who seemed to believe enough in him and his telegraph to advance another dollar.

As he came down to breakfast the next morning a young lady entered and came forward with a smile, exclaiming, " I have come to congratulate you." " Upon what?" inquired the professor. " Upon the passage of your bill," she replied. " Impossible! Its fate was sealed last evening. You must be mistaken." " Not at all," answered the young lady, the daughter of Morse's friend, the Commissioner of Patents, H. L. Ellsworth; "father sent me to tell you that your bill was passed. He remained until the session closed, and yours was the last bill but one acted upon, and it was passed just five minutes before the adjournment. And I am so glad to be able to be the first one to tell you. Mother says you must come home with me to breakfast."

Morse, overcome by the intelligence, promised that his young friend, the bearer of these good tidings, should send the first message over the first line of telegraph that was opened.

He writes to Alfred Vail that day: "The amount of business before the Senate rendered it more and more doubtful, as the session drew to a close, whether the House bill on the telegraph would be reached, and on the last day, March 3, 1843, I was advised by one of my Senatorial friends to make up my mind for failure, as he deemed it next to impossible that it could be reached before the adjournment. The bill, however, was reached a few minutes before midnight and passed. This was the turning point in the history of the telegraph. My personal funds were reduced to the fraction of a dollar, and, had the passage of the bill failed from any cause, there would have been little prospect of another attempt on my part to introduce to the world my new invention."

The appropriation by Congress having been made, Morse went to work with energy and delight to construct the first line of his electric telegraph. It was important that it should be laid where it would attract the attention of the government, and this consideration decided the question in favor of a line between Washington and Baltimore. He had as assistants Professor Gale and Professor J. C. Fisher. Mr. Vail was to devote his attention to making the instruments and the purchase of materials. Morse himself was general superintendent under the appointment of the government and gave attention to the minutest details. All disbursements passed through his hands. In point of accuracy, the preservation of vouchers, and presentation of accounts, General Washington himself was not more precise, lucid, and correct. Ezra Cornell, afterward one of the most successful constructors of telegraph lines, was employed to take charge of the work under Morse. Much time and expense were lost in consequence of following a plan for laying the wires in a leaden tube, and it was only when it was decided to string them on posts that work began to proceed rapidly.

In expectation of the meeting of the National Whig Convention, May 1, 1844, to nominate candidates for President and Vice-President, energy was redoubled, and by that time the wires were in working order twenty-two miles from Washington toward Baltimore. The day before the convention met, Professor Morse wrote to Vail that certain signals should mean the nomination of a particular candidate. The experiment was approaching its crisis. The con-

vention assembled and Henry Clay was nominated by acclamation to the Presidency. The
news was conveyed on the railroad to the
point reached by the telegraph and thence instantly transmitted over the wires to Washington. An hour afterward passengers arriving
at the capital, and supposing that they had
brought the first intelligence, were surprised to

Morse in his Study.
(From an old print.)

find that the announcement had been made already and that they were the bearers of old
news. The convention shortly afterward nominated Frelinghuysen as Vice-President, and
the intelligence was sent to Washington in the
same manner. Public astonishment was great
and many persons doubted that the feat could
have been performed. Before May had elapsed
the line reached Baltimore.

On the 24th of May, 1844, Morse was prepared

to put to final test the great experiment on which his mind had been laboring for twelve anxious years. Vail, his assistant, was at the Baltimore terminus. Morse had invited his friends to assemble in the chamber of the United States Supreme Court, where he had his instrument, from which the wires extended to Baltimore. He had promised his young friend, Miss Ellsworth, that she should send the first message over the wires. Her mother suggested the familiar words of scripture (Numbers, xxiii. 23), " What hath God wrought!" The words were chosen without consultation with the inventor, but were singularly the expression of his own sentiment and his own experience in bringing his work to successful accomplishment. Perfectly religious in his convictions, and trained from earliest childhood to believe in the special superintendence of Providence in the minutest affairs of man, he had acted throughout the whole of his struggles under the firm persuasion that God was working in him to do His own pleasure in this thing.

The first public messages sent were a notice to Silas Wright in Washington of his nomination to the office of Vice-President of the United States by the Democratic convention, then in session (May, 1844) in Baltimore, and his response declining it. Hendrick B. Wright, in a letter written to Mr. B. J. Lossing, says: " As the presiding officer of the body I read the despatch, but so incredulous were the members as to the authority of the evidence before them that the convention adjourned over to the following day to await the report of the committee sent over to Washington to get *reliable* information on the subject." Mr. Vail kept a diary in those early days of the telegraph, full of interesting reminiscences. It was often necessary, in order to convince incredulous visitors to the office that the questions and replies sent over the wire were not manufactured or agreed upon beforehand, to allow them to send their own remarks. When the committee just mentioned by Mr. Wright returned from Baltimore and confirmed the correctness of the report given by telegraph, the new invention received a splendid advertisement. The convention having reassembled in the morning, and the refusal of Wright to accept the nomination having been communicated, a conference was held between him and his friends through the medium of Morse's wires. In Washington Mr. Wright and Mr. Morse were closeted with the instrument; at Baltimore the committee of conference surrounded Vail with his instrument. Spectators and auditors were excluded. The committee communicated to Mr. Wright their reasons for urging his acceptance. In a moment he received their communication in writing and as quickly returned his answer. Again and again these confidential messages passed, and the result was finally announced to the convention that Mr. Wright was inflexible. Mr. Dallas then received the nomination and accepted it. The ticket thus nominated was successful at the election of that year. The original slips of paper on which some of the early messages were written are still preserved, among others this request: "As a rumor is prevalent here this morning that Mr. Eugene Boyle was shot at Baltimore last evening, Professor Morse will confer a great favor upon the family by making inquiry by means of his electro-magnetic telegraph if such is the fact."

The telegraph was shown at first without charge. During the session of 1844–1845 Congress made an appropriation of $8,000 to keep it in operation during the year, placing it under the supervision of the Postmaster-General, who, at the close of the session, ordered a tariff of charges of one cent for every four characters made through the telegraph. Mr. Vail was appointed operator for the Washington station and Mr. H. J. Rogers for Baltimore. This new order of things began April 1, 1845, the object being to test the profitableness of the enterprise. The first day's income was one cent; on the fifth day twelve and a half cents were received; on the seventh the receipts ran up to sixty cents; on the eighth to one dollar and thirty-two cents; on the ninth to one dollar and four cents. It is worthy of remark, as Mr. Vail notes, that the business done after the tariff was fixed was greater than when the service was gratuitous.

The telegraph was now a reality. Its completion was hailed with enthusiasm, and the newspapers lauded the inventor to the skies. Resolutions of thanks and applause were adopted by popular assemblies. It was a favorite idea with Professor Morse, from the inception of his enterprise, that the telegraph should belong to the government, and he sent a communication to Congress making a formal offer. The overture was not accepted, but the extension of the line from Baltimore to Philadelphia and then to New York was only a work of time. The aid of Congress was sought in vain. The appropriation of $8,000 was made, but further than that the government declined to go. The sum named as the price at which the Morse Company would sell the telegraph to the government was $100,000. The subject was discussed in the report of Cave Johnson, Postmaster-General under President Polk. He was a member of Congress when the bill came up before the House appropriating $30,000 for the experimental line, and was one of those who ridiculed the whole subject as unworthy of the notice of sensible men. As Postmaster-General he said in his report, after the experiment had succeeded to the satisfaction of mankind, that "the operation of a telegraph between Washington and Baltimore had not satisfied him that under any rate of postage that could be adopted its revenues could be made equal to its expenditures." Such an opinion, with the evidence then in the possession of the department, appears to be curious official blindness. But it was fortunate for the inventor that the telegraph was left to the private enterprise. Twenty-five years after the government had declined to take the telegraph at the price of $100,000, a project was started to establish lines of telegraph to be used by the government as part of the mail postal system. And in 1873 the Postmaster-General, Mr. Cresswell, said in his report that the entire first cost of all the lines in the country, including patents, was less than $10,000,000; but the property of the existing telegraph company was already well worth $50,000,000.

Morse's position was far easier than it had been for many years. His old friends, the artists of New York, rallied in force and laid before Congress a petition that the professor be employed to execute the painting to fill the panel at the Capitol assigned to Inman, who had been removed by death. But it came to nothing. Morse was never again to take the brush in hand. The first money that he received from his invention was the sum of $47, being his share of the amount paid for the right to use his patent on a short line from the Washington Post-office to the National Observatory. The use he made of the money was characteristic of the man. He sent it to the Rev. Dr. Sprole, then a pastor in Washington, requesting him to apply it for the benefit of his church.

Early in June, 1846, the line from Baltimore to Philadelphia was in operation, and that from Philadelphia to New York. Abroad the system was working its way steadily into favor. In France an appropriation of nearly half a million francs was made to introduce the Morse system. But meantime violations of Morse's rights were beginning to crop up on every side, both at home and abroad. In a letter to Daniel Lord, his lawyer, Morse says:

"The plot thickens all around me; I think a dénouement not far off. I remember your consoling me under these attacks with bidding me think that I had invented something worth contending for. Alas! my dear sir, what encouragement is there to an inventor if, after years of toil and anxiety, he has only purchased for himself the pleasure of being a target for every vile fellow to shoot at, and in proportion as his invention is of public utility, so much the greater effort is to be made to defame that the robbery may excite the less sympathy? I know, however, that beyond all this there is a clear sky; but the clouds may not break away till I am no longer personally interested, whether it be foul or fair. I wish not to complain, but I have feelings, and cannot play the Stoic if I would."

Perhaps the most painful chapter of Morse's life is the history of the lawsuits in which he was involved in defence of his rights. His reputation as well as his property were assailed. Exceedingly sensitive to these attacks, the suits that followed the success of the telegraph cost him inexpressible distress. It is some satisfaction to be able to record that after years of bitter controversy the final decision was favorable to the inventor. Honors began to pour in upon him from even the uttermost parts of the earth. The Sultan of Turkey was the first monarch to acknowledge Morse as a public benefactor. This was in 1848. The kings of Prussia and Wurtem-

burg and the Emperor of Austria each gave him
a gold medal, that of the first named being set in
a massive gold snuff-box.   In 1856 the Emperor
of the French made him a chevalier of the Legion of Honor.   Orders from Denmark, Spain,
Italy, Portugal soon followed.   In 1858 a special

The Siphon Recorder for Receiving Cable Messages—Office of the Commercial
Cable Company, 1 Broad Street, New York.

congress was called by the Emperor of the
French to devise a suitable testimonial of the
nation to Professor Morse.   Representatives
from ten sovereignties convened at Paris and by
a unanimous vote gave, in the aggregate, $80,000
as an honorary gratuity to Professor Morse.
The states participating in this testimonial were
France, Austria, Russia, Belgium, Holland, Swe-

den, Piedmont, the Holy See, Tuscany, and Turkey.

Professor Morse was one of the first to suggest and the first to carry out the use of a marine cable. During the summer of 1842 he had been making elaborate preparations for an experiment destined to give wonderful development to his invention. This was no less than a submarine wire, to demonstrate the fact that the current of electricity could be conducted as well under water as through the air. Of this he had entertained no doubt. "If I can make it work ten miles, I can make it go around the globe," was a favorite expression of his in the infancy of his enterprise. But he wished to prove it. He insulated his wire as well as he could with hempen strands well covered with pitch, tar, and india-rubber. In the course of the autumn he was prepared to put the question to the test of actual experiment. The wire was only the twelfth of an inch in diameter. About two miles of this, wound on a reel, was placed in a small row-boat, and with one man at the oars and Professor Morse at the stern, the work of paying out the cable was begun. It was a beautiful moonlight night, and those who had prolonged their evening rambles on the Battery must have wondered, as they watched the proceedings in the boat, what kind of fishing the two men could be engaged in that required so long a line. In somewhat less than two hours, on that eventful evening of October 18, 1842, the first cable was laid. Professor Morse returned to his lodgings and waited with some anxiety the time when he should be able to test the experiment fully and fairly. The next morning the New York *Herald* contained the following editorial announcement:

"MORSE'S ELECTRO-MAGNETIC TELEGRAPH.

"This important invention is to be exhibited in operation at Castle Garden between the hours of twelve and one o'clock to-day. One telegraph will be erected on Governor's Island and one at the Castle, and messages will be interchanged and orders transmitted during the day. Many have been incredulous as to the powers of this wonderful triumph of science and art. All such may now have an opportunity of fairly testing it. It is destined to work a complete revolution in the mode of transmitting intelligence throughout the civilized world."

At daybreak the professor was on the Battery, and had just demonstrated his success by the transmission of three or four characters between the termini of the line, when the communication was suddenly interrupted, and it was found impossible to send any messages through the conductor. The cause of this was evident when he observed no less than seven vessels lying along the line of the submerged cable, one of which, in getting under way, had raised it on her anchor. The sailors, unable to divine its meaning, hauled in about two hundred feet of it on deck, and finding no end, cut off that portion and carried it away with them. Thus ended the first attempt at submarine telegraphing. The crowd that had assembled on the Battery dispersed with jeers, most of them believing they had been made the victims of a hoax.

In a letter to John C. Spencer, then Secretary of the Treasury, in August, 1843, concerning electro-magnetism and its powers, he wrote:

"The practical inference from this law is that a telegraphic communication on the electro-magnetic plan may with certainty be established across the Atlantic Ocean. Startling as this may now seem, I am confident the time will come when this project will be realized."

In 1871 a statue of Professor Morse was erected in Central Park, New York, at the expense of the telegraph operators of the country. It was unveiled on June 10th with imposing ceremonies. There were delegates from every State in the Union, and from the British provinces. In the evening a public reception was given to the venerable inventor at the Academy of Music, at which William Orton, president of the Western Union Telegraph Company, presided, assisted by scores of the leading public men of the country as vice-presidents. The last scene was an impressive one. It was announced that the telegraphic instrument before the audience was then in connection with every other one of the ten thousand instruments in America. Then Miss Cornell, a young telegraphic operator, sent this message from the key: "Greeting and thanks to the telegraph fraternity throughout the world.

Glory to God in the highest, on earth peace, good-will to men." The venerable inventor, the personification of simplicity, dignity, and kindliness, was then conducted to the instrument, and touching the key, sent out: "S. F. B. MORSE." A storm of enthusiasm swept through the house as the audience rose, the ladies waving their handkerchiefs and the men cheering.

Professor Morse last appeared in public on February 22, 1872, when he unveiled the statue of Franklin, erected in Printing-house Square in New York. He died, after a short illness, on April 2, 1872, and was buried in Greenwood Cemetery. On the day of the funeral, April 5th, every telegraph office in the country was draped in mourning.

Professor Morse was twice married. His first wife died in 1825. In 1848 he married Sarah Elizabeth Griswold, of Poughkeepsie, who still lives. By the first marriage there were three children, one of whom, a son, survives. By the second marriage there were four children, three of whom are alive—a daughter and two sons. Miss Leila Morse, the daughter, was married in 1885 to Herr Franz Rummel, the eminent pianist. The last years of his life were eminently peaceful and happy. In the summer he lived at a place called Locust Grove, on the banks of the Hudson, near Poughkeepsie, and in the winter in a house at No. 5 West Twenty-second Street, a few doors west of Fifth Avenue. In recent years a marble tablet has been affixed to the front of the house, suitably inscribed.

No. 5 West Twenty-second Street, New York, where Morse Lived for Many Years and Died.

Morse's life in the country was very simple and quiet. His hour of rising was half-past six o'clock in the morning, and he was in his library alone until breakfast, at eight. He loved to hear the birds in their native songs, and he could distinguish the notes of each species, and would speak of the quality of their respective music. He spent most of the day in reading and writing, rarely taking exercise, except walking in his garden to visit his graperies, in which he took special pride, or to the stable to see if his horses were well cared for. He did not ride out regularly with his family, preferring the repose of his own grounds and the labors of his study. But when he walked or rode in the country, he was constantly disposed to speak of the beauty and glory around him, as revealing to his mind the beneficence, wisdom, and power of the infinite Creator, who had made all these things for the use and enjoyment of men.

One of his daughters writes of him in these simple and tender words : " He loved flowers. He would take one in his hand and talk for hours about its beauty, its wonderful construction, and the wisdom and love of God in making so many varied forms of life and color to please our eyes. In his later years he became deeply interested in the microscope and purchased one of great excellence and power. For whole hours, all the afternoon or evening, he would sit over it, examining flowers or the animalculæ in different fluids. Then he would gather his children about him and give us a sort of extempore lecture on the wonders of creation invisible to the naked eye, but so clearly brought to view by the magnifying power of the microscope. He was very fond of animals, cats, and birds in particular. He tamed a little flying-squirrel, and it became so fond of him that it would sit on his shoulder while he was at his studies and would eat out of his hand and sleep in his pocket. To this little animal he became so much attached that we took it with us to Europe, where it came to an untimely end, in Paris, by running into an open fire."

His biographer, Prime, says of him :

" In person Professor Morse was tall, slender, graceful, and attractive. Six feet in stature, he stood erect and firm, even in old age. His blue eyes were expressive of genius and affection. His nature was a rare combination of solid intellect and delicate sensibility. Thoughtful, sober, and quiet, he readily entered into the enjoyments of domestic and social life, indulging in sallies of humor, and readily appreciating and greatly enjoying the wit of others. Dignified in his intercourse with men, courteous and affable with the gentler sex, he was a good husband, a judicious father, a generous and faithful friend. He had the misfortune to incur the hostility of men who would deprive him of the merit and the reward of his labors. But his was the common fate of great inventors. He lived until his rights were vindicated by every tribunal to which they could be referred, and acknowledged by all civilized nations. And he died leaving to his children a spotless and illustrious name, and to his country the honor of having given birth to the only electro-magnetic recording telegraph whose line has gone out through all the earth and its words to the end of the world."

Charles Goodyear.

VI.

CHARLES GOODYEAR.

INDIA-RUBBER had been known for more than
a hundred years when Charles Goodyear undertook to make of it thousands of articles useful in
common life. So long ago as 1735 a party of
French astronomers discovered in Peru a curious tree that yielded the natives a peculiar gum
or sap which they collected in clay vessels.
This sap became hard when exposed to the sun,
and was used by the natives, who made different
articles of every-day use from it by dipping a
clay mould again and again into the liquid.
When the article was completed the clay mould
was broken to pieces and shaken out. In this
manner they made a kind of rough shoe and an
equally rough bottle. In some parts of South
America the natives presented their guests with
these bottles, which served as syringes for
squirting water. Articles thus made were liable
to become stiff and unmanageable in cold weather
and soft and sticky in warm. Upon getting back
to France the travellers directed the attention
of scientists to this remarkable gum, which was
afterward found in various parts of South America, and the chief supplies of which still come
from Brazil. About the beginning of the pres-

ent century this substance, known variously as cachuchu, caoutchouc, gum-elastic, and india-rubber, was first commercially introduced into Europe. It was regarded merely as a curiosity, chiefly useful for erasing pencil-marks. Ships from South America took it over as ballast. About the year 1820 it began to be used in France in the manufacture of suspenders and garters, india-rubber threads being mixed with the material used in weaving those articles. Some years later Mackintosh, an English manufacturer, used it in his famous water-proof coats, which were made by spreading a layer of the gum between two pieces of cloth.

About the same time a pair of india-rubber shoes were exhibited in Boston, where they were regarded as a curiosity; they were covered with gilt-foil to hide their natural ugliness. In 1823 a Boston merchant, engaged in the South American trade, imported five hundred pairs of these shoes, made by the natives of Para, and found no difficulty in selling them. In fact, this became a large business, although these shoes were terribly rough and clumsy and were not to be depended upon; in cold weather they became so hard that they could be used only after being thawed by the fire, and in summer they could be preserved only by keeping them on ice. If during the thawing process they were placed too near the fire, they would melt into a shapeless mass; and yet they cost from three to five dollars a pair.

In 1830 E. M. Chaffee, of Boston, the foreman

of a patent leather factory in that city, attempted to replace patent leather by a compound of india-rubber. He dissolved a pound of the gum in spirits of turpentine, added to the mixture enough lamp-black to produce a bright black color, and invented a machine for spreading this compound over cloth. When dried in the sun it produced a hard, smooth surface, flexible enough to be twisted into any shape without cracking. With the aid of a few capitalists, Chaffee organized, in 1833, a company called the Roxbury India-rubber Company, and manufactured an india-rubber cloth from which wagon-covers, piano-covers, caps, coats, shoes, and other articles were made. The product of the factory sold well, and the success of the Roxbury Company led to the establishment of a number of similar factories elsewhere. Apparently all who were engaged in the production of rubber goods were on the highway to wealth.

A day of disaster, however, came. Most of the goods produced in the winter of 1833–1834 became worthless during the following summer. The shoes melted to a soft mass and the caps, wagon-covers, and coats became sticky and useless. To make matters worse they emitted an odor so offensive that it was necessary to bury them in the ground. Twenty thousand dollars' worth of these goods were thrown back on the hands of the Roxbury Company alone, and the directors were appalled by the ruin that threatened them. It was useless to go on manufacturing goods that might prove worthless at any moment. India-rubber stock fell rapidly, and by the end of 1836 there was not a solvent rubber company in the Union, the stockholders losing about $2,000,000. People came to detest the very name of india-rubber.

One day, in 1834, a Philadelphia hardware merchant, named Charles Goodyear, was led by curiosity to buy a rubber life-preserver. And thus began for this unfortunate genius nearly twenty-five years of struggle, misery, and disappointment. Charles Goodyear was born in New Haven, Conn., December 29, 1800. When a boy his father moved to Philadelphia, where he engaged in the hardware business, and upon becoming of age, Charles Goodyear joined him as a partner. In the panic of 1836–1837 the house went down. Goodyear's attention had been attracted for several years by the wonderful success of the india-rubber companies. Upon examining his life-preserver he discovered a defect in the inflating valve and made an improved one. Going to New York with this device, he called on the agent of the Roxbury Company and, explaining it to him, offered to sell it to the company. The agent was impressed with the improvement, but instead of buying it, told the inventor the real state of the india-rubber business of the country, then on the verge of a collapse. He urged Goodyear to exert his inventive skill in discovering some means of imparting durability to india-rubber goods, and assured him that if he could find a process to effect that end, he could sell it at his own price.

He explained the processes then in use and their imperfections.

Goodyear forgot all about his disappointment in failing to sell his valve, and went home intent upon experiments to make gum-elastic durable. From that time until the close of his life he devoted himself solely to this work. He was thirty-five years old, feeble in health, a bankrupt in business, and had a young family depending upon him. The industry in which he now engaged was one in which thousands of persons had found ruin. The firm of which he had been a member owed $30,000, and upon his return to Philadelphia he was arrested for debt and compelled to live within prison limits. He began his experiments at once. The price of the gum had fallen to five cents per pound, so that he had no difficulty in getting sufficient of it to begin work. By melting and working it thoroughly and rolling it out upon a stone table, he succeeded in producing sheets of india-rubber that seemed to him to possess new properties. A friend loaned him enough money to manufacture a number of shoes which at first seemed to be all that could be desired. Fearful, however, of coming trouble, Goodyear put his shoes away until the following summer, when the warm weather reduced them to a mass of so offensive an odor that he was glad to throw them away. His friend was so thoroughly disheartened by this failure as to refuse to have anything more to do with Goodyear's scheme. The inventor, nevertheless, kept on.

It occurred to him that there must be some substance which, mixed with the gum, would render it durable, and he began to experiment with almost every substance that he could lay his hands on. All proved total failures with the exception of magnesia. By mixing half a pound of magnesia with a pound of the gum he produced a substance whiter than the pure gum, which was at first as firm and flexible as leather, and out of which he made beautiful book-covers and piano-covers. It looked as if he had solved the problem; but in a month his pretty product was ruined. Heat caused it to soften; fermentation then set in, and finally it became as hard and brittle as thin glass. His stock of money was now exhausted. He was forced to pawn all his own valuables and even the trinkets of his wife. But he felt sure that he was on the road to success and would eventually win both fame and fortune. He removed his family to the country, and set out for New York, where he hoped to find someone willing to aid him in carrying his experiments further. Here he met two acquaintances, one of whom offered him the use of a room in Gold Street as a workshop, and the other, a druggist, agreed to let him have on credit such chemicals as he needed. He now boiled the gum, mixed with magnesia, in quicklime and water, and as a result obtained firm, smooth sheets that won him a medal at the fair of the American Institute in 1835. He seemed on the point of success, and easily sold all the sheets he could manufacture, when, to his dismay, he discovered that a drop of the weakest acid, such as the juice of an apple or diluted vinegar, would reduce his new compound to the old sticky substance that had baffled him so often.

His first important discovery on the road to real success was the result of accident. He liked pretty things, and it was a constant effort with him to make his productions as attractive to the eye as possible. Upon one occasion, while bronzing a piece of rubber cloth, he applied aqua fortis to it for the purpose of removing part of the bronze. It took away the bronze, but it also destroyed the cloth to such a degree that he supposed it ruined and threw it away. A day or two later, happening to pick it up, he was astonished to find that the rubber had undergone a remarkable change, and that the effect of the acid had been to harden it to such an extent that it would now stand a degree of heat which would have melted it before. Aqua fortis contained sulphuric acid. Goodyear was thus on the threshold of his great discovery of vulcanizing rubber. He called his new process the "curing" of india-rubber.

The "cured" india-rubber was subjected to many tests and passed through them successfully, thus demonstrating its adaptability to many important uses. Goodyear readily obtained a patent for his process, and a partner with a large capital was found ready to aid him. He hired the old india-rubber works on Staten Island and opened a salesroom in Broadway. He was thrown back for six weeks at this important time by an accident which happened to him while experimenting with his fabrics and which came near causing his death. Just as he was recovering and preparing to begin the manufacture of his goods on a large scale the terrible commercial crisis of 1837 swept over the country, and by destroying his partner's fortune at one blow, reduced Goodyear to absolute beggary. His family had joined him in New York, and he was entirely without the means of supporting them. As the only resource at hand he decided to pawn an article of value—one of the few which he possessed—in order to raise money to procure one day's supply of provisions. At the very door of the pawnbroker's shop he met one of his creditors, who kindly asked if he could be of any further assistance to him. Weak with hunger and overcome by the generosity of his friend the poor man burst into tears and replied that, as his family was on the point of starvation, a loan of $15 would greatly oblige him. The money was given him on the spot and the necessity for visiting the pawnbroker averted for several days longer. Still he was a frequent visitor to that person during the year, and one by one the relics of his better days disappeared. Another friend loaned him $100, which enabled him to remove his family to Staten Island, in the neighborhood of the abandoned rubber works, which the owners gave him permission to use so far as he could. He contrived in this way to manufacture enough of his "cured" cloth, which sold readily, to enable him to keep his family from starvation. He made repeated efforts to induce capitalists to come to the factory and see his samples and the process by which they were made, but no one would venture near him. There had been money enough lost in such experiments, these acquaintances said, and they were determined to risk no more.

Indeed, in all the broad land there was but one man who had the slightest hope of accomplishing anything with india-rubber, and that one was Charles Goodyear. His friends regarded him as a monomaniac. He not only manufactured his cloth, but even dressed in clothes made of it, wearing it for the purpose of testing its durability, as well as of advertising it. He was certainly an odd figure, and in his appearance justified the remark of one of his friends, who, upon being asked how Mr. Goodyear could be recognized, replied: "If you see a man with an india-rubber coat on, india-rubber shoes, and india-rubber cap, and in his pocket an india-rubber purse with not a cent in it, that is Goodyear."

In September, 1837, a new gleam of hope lit up his pathway. A friend having loaned him a small sum of money he went to Roxbury, taking with him some of his best specimens. Although the Roxbury Company had gone down with a fearful crash, Mr. Chaffee, the inventor of the first process of making rubber goods in this country, was still firm in his faith that india-rubber would at some future time justify the expectations of its earliest friends. He welcomed Goodyear cordially and allowed him to use the abandoned works of the company for his experiments. The result was that Goodyear succeeded in making shoes and cloths of india-rubber of a quality so much better than any that had yet been seen in America that the hopes of the friends of india-rubber were raised to a high point. Offers to purchase rights for certain portions of the country came in rapidly, and by the

Calenders Heated Internally by Steam, for Spreading India Rubber into Sheets or upon Cloth, called the "Chaffee Machine."

sale of them Goodyear realized between four and five thousand dollars. He was now able to bring his family to Roxbury, and for the time fortune seemed to smile upon him.

His success was but temporary, however. He obtained an order from the general Government for one hundred and fifty india-rubber mail-bags, which he succeeded in producing, and as they came out smooth, highly polished, hard, well shaped, and entirely impervious to moisture, he was delighted and summoned his friends to inspect and admire them. All who saw them pronounced them a perfect success, but alas! in a single month they began to soften and ferment, and finally became useless. Poor Goodyear's hopes were dashed to the ground. It was found that the aqua fortis merely "cured" the surface of the material, and that only very thin cloth made in this way was durable. His other goods began to prove worthless and his promising business came to a sudden and disastrous end. All his possessions were seized and sold for debt, and once more he was reduced to poverty. His position was even worse than before, for his family had increased in size and his aged father also had become dependent upon him for support.

Friends, relatives, and even his wife, all demanded that he should abandon his empty dreams and turn his attention to something that would yield a support to his family. Four years of constant failure, added to the unfortunate experience of those who had preceded him, ought to convince him, they said, that he was hoping against hope. Hitherto his conduct, certainly had been absurd, though they admitted that he was to some extent excused for it by his partial success; but to persist in it would be criminal. The inventor was driven to despair, and being a man of tender feelings and ardently devoted to his family, might have yielded to them had he not felt that he was nearer than ever to the discovery of the secret that had eluded him so long.

Just before the failure of his mail-bags had brought ruin upon him, he had taken into his employ a man named Nathaniel Hayward, who had been the foreman of the old Roxbury works, and who was still in charge of them when Goodyear came to Roxbury, and was making a few rubber articles on his own account. He hardened his compound by mixing a little powdered sulphur with the gum, or by sprinkling sulphur over the rubber cloth and drying it in the sun. He declared that the process had been revealed to him in a dream, but could give no further account of it. Goodyear was astonished to find that the sulphur cured the india-rubber as thoroughly as the aqua fortis, the principal objection being that the sulphurous odor of the goods was frightful in hot weather. Hayward's process was really the same as that employed by Goodyear, the "curing" of the india-rubber being due in each case to the agency of the sulphur, the principal difference between them being that Hayward's goods were dried by the sun and Goodyear's with nitric acid. Hayward set so small a value upon his discovery that he readily sold it to his new employer.

Goodyear felt that he had now all but conquered his difficulties. It was plain that sulphur was the great controller of india-rubber, for he had proved that when applied to thin cloth it would render it available for most purposes. The problem that now remained was how to mix sulphur and the gum in a mass, so that every part of the rubber should be subjected to the agency of the sulphur. He experimented for weeks and months with the most intense eagerness, but the mystery completely baffled him. His friends urged him to go to work to do something for his family, but he could not turn back. The goal was almost in sight, and he felt that he would be false to his mission were he to abandon his labors now. To the world he seemed a crack-brained dreamer, and some there were who, seeing the distress of his family, did not hesitate to apply still harsher names to him. Had it been merely wealth that he was working for, doubtless he would have turned back and sought some other means of obtaining it; but he sought more. He felt that he had a mission to fulfil, and that no one else could perform it.

He was right. A still greater success was about to crown his labors, but in a manner far different from his expectations. His experiments had developed nothing; chance was to make the revelation. It was in the spring of 1839, and in the following manner: Standing before a stove in a store at Woburn, Mass., he was explaining to some acquaintances the properties of a piece of sulphur-cured india-rubber which he held in his hand. They listened to him good-naturedly, but with evident incredulity, when suddenly he dropped the rubber on the stove, which was red hot. His old clothes would have melted instantly from contact with such heat; but, to his surprise, this piece underwent no such change. In amazement he examined it, and found that while it had charred or shrivelled like leather, it had not soft-

ened at all.   The bystanders attached no importance to this phenomenon, but to him it was a
revelation.   He renewed his experiments with
enthusiasm, and in a little while established the
facts that india-rubber, when mixed with sulphur
and exposed to a certain degree of heat for a
specified time, would not melt or soften at any
degree of heat ; that it would only char at two
hundred and eighty degrees, and that it would
not stiffen from exposure to any extent of cold.
The difficulty now consisted in finding out the
exact degree of heat necessary for the perfecting
of the rubber and the exact length of time required for the heating.

   He made this discovery in his darkest days,
when, in fact, he was in constant danger of arrest
for debt, having already been a frequent inmate
of the debtors' prison.   He was in the depths of
bitter poverty and in such feeble health that he
was constantly haunted by the fear of dying before he had perfected his discovery—before he
had fulfilled his mission.   He needed an apparatus for producing a high and uniform heat for his
expériments, and he was unable to obtain it.   He
used to bake his compound in his wife's bread-
oven and steam it over the spout of her tea-
kettle, and to press the kitchen fire into his service so far as it would go.   When this failed, he
would go down to the shops in the vicinity of
Woburn and beg to be allowed to use the ovens
and boilers after working hours were over.   The
workmen regarded him as a lunatic, but were too
good-natured to deny him the request.   Finally

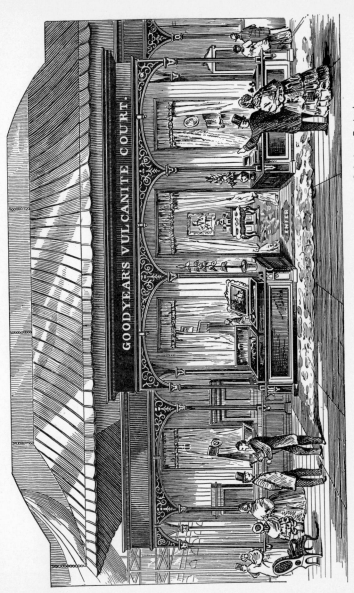

Charles Goodyear's Exhibition of Hard India Rubber Goods at the Crystal Palace, Sydenham, England.

(From a print published at the time.)

he induced a bricklayer to make him an oven, and paid him in masons' aprons of india-rubber. The oven was a failure. Sometimes it would turn out pieces of perfectly vulcanized cloth, and again the goods would be charred and ruined. Goodyear was in despair.

All this time he lived on the charity of his friends. His neighbors pretended to lend him money, but in reality gave him the means of keeping his family from starvation. He has declared that all the while he felt sure he would, before long, be able to pay them back, but they have declared with equal emphasis that, at that time, they never expected to witness his success. He was yellow and shrivelled in face, with a gaunt, lean figure, and his habit of wearing an india-rubber coat, which was charred and blackened from his frequent experiments with it, gave him a wild and singular appearance. People shook their heads solemnly when they saw him, and said that the mad-house was the proper place for him.

The winter of 1839–40 was long and severe. At the opening of the season Goodyear received a letter from a house in Paris, making him a handsome offer for the use of his process of curing india-rubber with aqua fortis. Here was a chance for him to rise out of his misery. A year before he would have closed with the offer, but since then he had discovered the effects of sulphur and heat on his compound, and had passed far beyond the aqua-fortis stage. Disappointment and want had not warped his conscience, and he at once declined to enter into any arrangements with the French house, informing them that although the process they desired to purchase was a valuable one, it was about to be entirely replaced by another which he was then on the point of perfecting, and which he would gladly sell them as soon as he had completed it. His friends declared that he was mad to refuse such an offer; but he replied that nothing would induce him to sell a process which he knew was about to be rendered worthless by still greater discoveries.

A few weeks later a terrible snow-storm passed over the land, one of the worst that New England had ever known, and in the midst of it Goodyear made the appalling discovery that he had not a particle of fuel or a mouthful of food in the house. He was ill enough to be in bed himself, and his purse was entirely empty. It was a terrible position, made worse, too, by the fact that his friends who had formerly aided him had turned from him, vexed with his pertinacity, and abandoned him to his fate. In his despair he bethought him of a mere acquaintance named Coleridge, who lived several miles from his cottage, and who but a few days before had spoken to him with more of kindness than he had received of late. This gentleman, he thought, would aid him in his distress, if he could but reach his house, but in such a snow the journey seemed hopeless to a man in his feeble health. Still the effort must be made. Nerved by despair, he set out and pushed his way resolutely through the heavy drifts.

The way was long, and it seemed to him that he would never accomplish it. Often he fell prostrate on the snow, almost fainting with fatigue and hunger, and again he would sit down wearily in the road, feeling that he would gladly die if his discovery were but completed. At length, however, he reached the end of his journey, and fortunately found his acquaintance at home. To this gentleman he told the story of his discovery, his hopes, his struggles, and his present sufferings, and implored him to help him. Mr. Coleridge listened to him kindly, and after expressing the warmest sympathy for him, loaned him money enough to support his family during the severe weather and to enable him to continue his experiments.

Seeing no prospect of success in Massachusetts, he now resolved to make a desperate effort to get to New York, feeling confident that the specimens he could take with him would convince someone of the superiority of his new method. He was beginning to understand the cause of his many failures, but he saw clearly that his compound could not be worked with certainty without expensive apparatus. It was a very delicate operation, requiring exactness and promptitude. The conditions upon which success depended were many, and the failure of one spoiled all. It cost him thousands of failures to learn that a little acid in his sulphur caused the blistering; that his compound must be heated almost immediately after being mixed or it would never vulcanize; that a portion of white lead in the compound greatly facilitated the operation and improved the result; and when he had learned these facts, it still required costly and laborious experiments to devise the best methods of compounding his ingredients in the best proportions, the best mode of heating, the proper duration of the heating, and the various useful effects that could be produced by varying

COUNCIL MEDAL OF THE EXHIBITION.
C. GOODYEAR. CLASS XXVIII.

1851.

the proportions and the degree of heat. He tells us that many times when, by exhausting every resource, he had prepared a quantity of his compound for heating, it was spoiled because he could not, with his inadequate apparatus, apply the heat soon enough.

To New York, then, he directed his thoughts. Merely to get there cost him a severer and a longer effort than men in general are capable of making. First he walked to Boston, ten miles distant, where he hoped to borrow from an old acquaintance $50, with which to provide for his family and pay his fare to New York. He not only failed in this, but he was arrested for debt and thrown into prison. Even in prison, while his old father was negotiating to procure his release, he labored to interest men of capital in his discovery, and made proposals for founding a factory in Boston. Having obtained his liberty, he went to a hotel and spent a week in vain efforts to effect a small loan. Saturday night came, and with it his hotel bill, which he had no means of discharging. In an agony of shame and anxiety, he went to a friend and entreated the sum of $5 to enable him to return home. He was met with a point-blank refusal. In the deepest dejection, he walked the streets till late in the night, and strayed at length, almost beside himself, to Cambridge, where he ventured to call upon a friend and ask shelter for the night. He was hospitably entertained, and the next morning walked wearily home, penniless and despairing. At the door of his house a member of his family met him with the news that his youngest child, two years old, whom he had left in perfect health, was dying. In a few hours he had in his house a dead child, but not the means of burying it, and five living dependents without a morsel of food to give them. A storekeeper near by had promised to supply the family, but, discouraged by the unforeseen length of the father's absence, he had that day refused to trust them further. In these terrible circumstances he applied to a friend, upon whose generosity he knew he could rely, one who never failed him. He received in reply a letter of severe and cutting reproach, enclosing $7, which his friend explained was given only out of pity for his innocent and suffering family. A stranger who chanced to be present when this letter arrived sent them a barrel of flour, a timely and blessed relief. The next day the family followed on foot the remains of the little child to the grave.

This was about the darkest hour of poor Goodyear's life, but it was before the dawn. He managed to obtain $50, with which he went to New York, and succeeded in interesting two brothers, William and Emory Rider, in his discoveries. They agreed to advance to him a certain sum to complete his experiments. By means of this aid he was enabled to keep his family from want, and his experiments were pursued with greater ease and certainty. His brother-in-law, William De Forrest, a rich wool manufacturer, also came to his aid, now that success seemed in view. Nevertheless, the experiments of that and the following year cost nearly $50,000. Thanks to this timely aid, he was able in 1844, ten years after beginning his work, to produce perfect vulcanized india-rubber with economy and certainty. To the end of his life he was at work, however, endeavoring to improve the material and apply it to new uses. He took out more than sixty patents covering different processes of making rubber goods.

If Goodyear had been a man of business in-
stincts and habits, the years following the completion of his great work might have brought him
an immense fortune ; but everywhere he seems
to have been unfortunate in protecting his rights.
In France and England he lost his patent rights
by technical defects.   In the latter country another man, who had received a copy of the

GRANDE MEDAILLE D'HONNEUR.
EXPOSITION UNIVERSELLE DE 1855.

Donne pour la Decouverte de la Vulcanisation et Durcissement du Caoutchouc.
FACSIMILE GOLD

American patent, actually applied and obtained
the English rights in his own name.   Goodyear,
however, obtained the great council medal at
the London Exhibition of 1851, a grand medal at
Paris, in 1855, and later the ribbon of the Legion
of Honor.   In this country he was scarcely less
unfortunate.   His patents were infringed right
and left, he was cheated by business associates
and plundered of the profits of his invention.
The United States Commissioner of Patents, in
1858, thus spoke of his losses:

" No inventor, probably, has ever been so harassed, so trampled upon, so plundered by that sordid and licentious class of infringers known in the parlance of the world as ' pirates.' The spoliation of their incessant guerilla warfare upon his defenceless rights has unquestionably amounted to millions."

Goodyear died in New York in July, 1860, worn out with work and disappointment. Neither Europe nor America seemed disposed to accord him any reward or credit for having made one of the greatest discoveries of the time. Notwithstanding his invention, which has made millions for those engaged in working it, he died insolvent, and left his family heavily in debt. A few years after his death an effort was made to procure from Congress an extension of his patent for the benefit of his family and creditors. The opposition of the men who had grown rich and powerful by successfully infringing his rights prevented that august body from doing justice in the matter and the effort came to nothing.

VII.

JOHN ERICSSON.

CAPTAIN JOHN ERICSSON, although not by birth an American, rendered such signal services to this country and lived here for so many years that we may fairly consider him in the light of an American inventor. The inventions to which he devoted the best years of his life were made in this country. He loved America, he died here, and though his ashes have been sent back to Sweden, the world of Europe, in common with ourselves, probably thinks of Ericsson as an American.

By the roadside near a mountain hamlet of Central Sweden stands a pyramid of iron cast from ore dug from the adjacent mines and set upon a base of granite quarried from the hills which overlook the valley. This monument bears the information that two brothers, Nils Ericsson and John Ericsson, were born in a miner's hut at that place, respectively, January 31, 1802, and July 31, 1803. Nils Ericsson was a man of unusual distinction, who held high position in Sweden as engineer of the canals and railroads of the kingdom. The name of his brother is known the world over. These two notable Swedes were sons of Olof Ericsson, a Swedish

John Ericsson.

miner. Poverty was one of the bits of good fortune that fell to the lot of the two boys, and among John's earliest recollections is that of the seizure of their household effects by the sheriff. The mother was a woman of intelligence and somewhat acquainted with the literature of her time. In boyhood John Ericsson worked in the iron mines of Central Sweden. Machinery was his first love and his last. Before he was eleven years old, during the winter of 1813, he had produced a miniature saw-mill of ingenious construction, and had planned a pumping-engine designed to keep the mines free from water. The frame of the saw-mill was of wood; the saw-blade was made from a watch-spring and was moved by a crank made from a broken tin spoon. A file, borrowed from a neighboring blacksmith, a gimlet, and a jack-knife were the only tools used in this work. His pumping-engine was a more ambitious affair, to be operated by a wind-mill.

The family then lived in the wilderness, surrounded by a pine forest, where Ericsson's father was engaged in selecting timber for the lock-gates of a canal. A quill and a pencil were the boy's tools in the way of drawing materials. He made compasses of birch wood. A pair of steel tweezers were converted into a drawing-pen. Ericsson had never seen a wind-mill, but following as well as he could the description of those who had, he succeeded in constructing on paper the mechanism connecting the crank of a wind-mill with the pump-lever. The plan, conceived

John Ericsson's Birthplace and Monument.

and executed under such circumstances by a mere boy, attracted the attention of Count Platen, president of the Gotha Ship Canal, on which Ericsson's father was employed, and when Ericsson was twelve years old he was made a member of the surveying party carrying out the canal work and put in charge of a section. Six hundred of the royal troops looked for directions in their daily work to this boy, one of his attendants being a man who followed him with a stool, upon which he stood to use the surveying instruments. The amusements of this boy engineer, even at the age of fifteen, are indicated by a portfolio of drawings made in his leisure moments, giving maps of the most important parts of the canal, three hundred miles in length, and showing all the machinery used in its construction. His precocity was, however, the normal and healthy development of a mind as fond of mechanical principles as Raphael was of color.

It was in 1811 that Ericsson made his first scale drawing of the famous Sunderland Iron Bridge, and from that time on his career in Sweden was a brilliant one. After serving as an engineer upon the Gotha Canal he became an officer in the Swedish army, from which circumstance he got his title of captain. Most government work was then done by army officers, especially in field surveying. The appointments of government surveyors being offered soon afterward to competitive examination among the officers of the army, Ericsson went to Stockholm and entered the lists. Detailed maps of fifty square miles of Swedish territory, still upon file at Stockholm, show his skill. Though his work as a surveyor exceeded that of any of his companions, he was not satisfied. He sought an outlet for his superfluous activity in preparing the drawings and engraving sixty-four large plates for a work illustrating the Gotha Canal. His faculty for invention was shown here by the construction of a machine-engraver, with which eighteen copper-plates were completed by his own hand within a year.

From engraving young Ericsson turned his attention to experiments with flame as a means of producing mechanical power, and it is interesting to note that forty years afterward a large part of his income in this country was derived from his gas- or flame-engine, thousands of which are now in use in New York City alone for pumping water up to the tops of the houses. His early flame-engine, as it was called, turned out so well that after building one of ten horse-power, he obtained leave of absence to go to England to introduce the invention. He never returned to Sweden for any length of time, although he remained a Swede at heart, and many Swedish orders and decorations have been conferred upon him. In addition to the monument near Ericsson's birthplace, already mentioned, the government has erected a granite shaft, eighteen feet high, in front of the cottage in which he was born. This shaft, bearing the inscription, "John Ericsson was born here in 1803," was dedicated on September 3, 1867, when work was suspended in the neighboring mines and iron furnaces, and a holiday was held in honor of Sweden's famous son. Poems were read, the chief engineer of the mining district delivered an oration, and Dr. Pallin, a savant from Philipstad, reminded his hearers that seven cities in Greece contended for the honor of being Homer's birthplace. "Certificates of baptism did not then exist," said Dr. Pallin, "and there is no doubt with us as to Ericsson's birthplace; yet to guard against all accidents we have here placed a record of baptism weighing eighty thousand pounds." The monument stands on an isthmus between two lakes surrounded by green hills.

Ericsson's life in England began in 1826. Fortune did not smile upon his efforts to introduce his flame-engine, for the coal fire which had to be used in England was too severe for the working parts of the apparatus. But Ericsson possessed a capacity for hard work that recognized no obstacles. He undertook a new series of experiments which resulted finally in the completion of an engine which was patented and sold to John Braithwaite. Young Ericsson's capacity for work and for keeping half a dozen experiments in view at the same time seems to have been as remarkable in those early days as when he became famous. Records of the London Patent Office credit him with invention after invention. Among these were a pumping-engine on a new principle; engines with surface condensers and no smoke-stack, as applied to the

The Novelty Locomotive, built by Ericsson to compete with Stephenson's Rocket, 1829.

steamship Victory in 1828; an apparatus for
making salt from brine; for propelling boats
on canals; a hydrostatic weighing machine, to
which the Society of Arts awarded a prize; an
instrument to be used in taking deep-sea sound-
ings; a file-cutting machine. The list covers
some fourteen patented inventions and forty machines.

Perhaps his most important work at this period was a device for creating artificial draught
in locomotives, to which aid the development of
our railroad owes much. In 1829 the Liverpool
& Manchester Railroad offered a prize of $2,500
for the best locomotive capable of doing certain work. The prize was taken by Stephenson
with his famous Rocket; but his sharpest com-
petitor in this contest was John Ericsson. Four
locomotives entered the contest. The London
Times of October 8, 1829, speaks highly of the
Novelty, the locomotive entered by Messrs.
Braithwaite & Ericsson, saying: "It was the
lightest and most elegant carriage on the road
yesterday, and the velocity with which it moved
surprised and amazed every beholder. It shot
along the line at the amazing rate of thirty miles
an hour. It seemed indeed to fly, presenting
one of the most sublime spectacles of human
ingenuity and human daring the world ever
beheld."

The railroad directors, at whose invitation this
test was made, had asked for ten miles an hour;
Ericsson gave them thirty. The excitement of
the witnesses found vent in loud cheers. Within

an hour the shares of the railroad company rose ten per cent., and the young engineer might well have considered his fortune made. But although

Ericsson on his Arrival in England, aged twenty-three.

he had beaten his rival ten miles an hour, the judges determined to make traction power, rather than speed, the critical test, and the prize was awarded to Stephenson's Rocket, which

drew seventeen tons for seventy miles at the rate
of thirteen miles an hour. Stephenson's engine
weighed twice as much as Ericsson's. Neverthe-

Mrs. John Ericsson, née Amelia Byam.
(From an early daguerreotype.)

less Ericsson's success with the Novelty was
such as to keep him busy in this particular field.
He followed it up with a steam fire-engine that
astonished London at the burning of the Argyle

Rooms, in 1829, when for the first time, as one of the local papers remarked, " fire was extinguished by the mechanical power of fire." Another engine, of larger power, built for the King of Prussia, soon after rendered excellent service in Berlin, and a third was built for Liverpool in 1830. Ten years afterward the Mechanics' Institute of New York awarded a gold medal to Ericsson as a prize for the best plan of a steam-engine.

Disappointed in his ill success with inventions pertaining to locomotives, Ericsson now turned his attention to his early flame-engine, and the working model of a caloric engine of five-horse power soon attracted the attention of London. At first there seemed to be a great future for engines upon this principle, but after many years of experiments, at great expense, Ericsson found that the principle was useful only for purposes requiring small power. In 1851 he built a heat-engine for the ship Ericsson, a vessel two hundred and sixty feet in length, and tells the result as follows : " The ship after completion made a successful trip from New York to Washington and back during the winter season ; but the average speed at sea proving insufficient for commercial purposes, the owners, with regret, acceded to my proposition to remove the costly machinery, although it had proved perfect as a mechanical combination. The resources of modern engineering having been exhausted in producing the motors of the caloric ship, the important question, Can heated air, as a mechan-

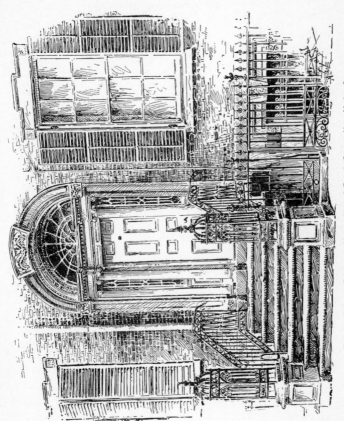

Exterior View of Ericsson's House, No. 36 Beach Street, New York, 1890.

ical motor, compete on a large scale with steam?
has forever been set at rest. The commercial
world is indebted to American enterprise for
having settled a question of such vital importance. The marine engineer has thus been encouraged to renew his efforts to perfect the
steam-engine without fear of rivalry from a motor depending on the dilation of atmospheric air
by heat."

Before leaving this question of heat-engines
and passing to the more important inventions by
which Ericsson will be remembered, it may be
as well to say a few words concerning the solar-
engines to which he devoted many years' time,
and one of which I saw in operation in the back
yard of the pleasant old house in Beach Street,
opposite the freight depot of the Hudson River
Railroad. This house, by the way, which Ericsson occupied for nearly forty years, faced on St.
John's Park, the pleasant square which was afterward filled up by the railroad company. Toward the last years of Ericsson's life the neighborhood became anything but a pleasant one to
live in; it was dirty and noisy. Nevertheless
Ericsson refused to move. Perhaps the unpleas-
antness of the surroundings made him the recluse
he was. It is not surprising that he should have
been attracted by the possibility of obtaining
power from the heat of the sun. In an early
pamphlet on the subject he says: " There is a
rainless region extending from the northwestern
coast of Africa to Mongolia, nine thousand miles
in length and nearly one thousand miles wide.

In the Western Hemisphere, Lower California,
the table-lands of Guatemala, and the west coast
of South America, for a distance of more than two
thousand miles, suffer from a continuous radiant

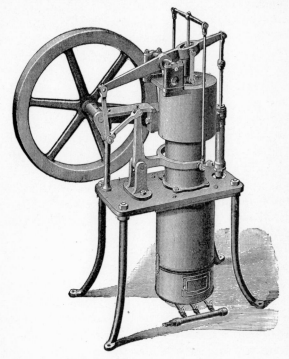

Solar-engine Adapted to the Use of Hot Air.
(Patented as a pumping-engine, 1880.)

heat." Ericsson estimated that the mechanical
power that would result from utilizing the solar
heat on a strip of land a single mile wide and
eight thousand miles long would suffice to keep
twenty-two million solar-engines, of one hundred

horse-power each, going nine hours a day. He believed that with the exhaustion of European coal-fields the day for the solar-engine would come, and that those countries which possessed unfailing sunshine, such as Egypt, would displace England, France, and Germany as the manufacturing powers of the world, for the European would have to move his machinery to the borders of the Nile. By concentrating the rays of the sun upon a small copper boiler filled with air Ericsson was enabled to work a little motor, and for some years he also attempted to produce steam by means of heat from the sun. He was not successful, however, in making anything of commercial value in this direction, and so far as I have been able to learn none of the tropical countries invited by him to take up the problem for its own benefit responded to the invitation.

Ericsson's studies and improvements of the screw as a means of propelling boats began in England. A model boat, two feet long, fitted up with two screws, was launched in a London bath-house, and, supplied by steam from a boiler placed at the side of the tank, was sent around at a speed estimated at six miles an hour. Ericsson was so delighted with it that he built a boat eight feet by forty, armed with two propellers, in the hope that the British Admiralty might adopt the invention. This boat went through the water at the rate of ten miles an hour, or seven miles an hour towing a schooner of one hundred and forty tons burden. He invited the Admiralty to see the work of his screw. Steaming up to Somerset House with his little vessel, Ericsson took the Admiralty barge in tow, to the wonder of the watermen, who could make nothing of the novel craft with no apparent means of propulsion. The British Admiralty, however, was not easily convinced. These wiseacres said nothing, but Ericsson professed to have heard that their verdict was against him because one of the authorities of the board decided that "even if the propeller had the power of propelling a vessel it would be found altogether useless in practice, because the power, being applied to the stern, it would be absolutely impossible to make the vessel steer."

This official blindness cost England the services of the inventor. The United States happened to have as consul in Liverpool at that day (1837) Mr. Francis B. Ogden, a pioneer in steam navigation on the Ohio River. Ogden saw Ericsson's invention and introduced him to Captain Robert F. Stockton, of the United States Navy. With Stockton, seeing was believing, and when he returned from a trip on Ericsson's boat, he exclaimed: "I do not want the opinion of your scientific men. What I have seen to-day satisfies me." Before the vessel had completed her trip, Ericsson received from Stockton an order for two boats. Upon Stockton's assurance that the United States would try his propeller upon a large scale, Ericsson closed up his affairs in England and embarked for the United States. Through the good offices of Stockton, but after considerable delay, a vessel called the

Princeton was ordered and completed. She carried a number of radical improvements destined to make a revolution in naval warfare. The boilers and engines were below the water-line, out of the way of shot and shell. The smoke-stack was a telescopic affair, replacing the tall pipe that formed so conspicuous a target upon the old boats. Centrifugal blowers in the hold, worked by separate engines, secured increased draught for the furnaces. The Princeton was a wonder, and everyone was ready to praise the inventive genius of Ericsson and the daring of Captain Stockton in adopting so many radical novelties. An entry in the diary of John Quincy Adams, dated February 28, 1844, tells the sad story of the public exhibition of the Princeton at Washington:

" I went into the chamber of the Committee of Manufactures and wrote there till six. Dined with Mr. Grinnell and Mr. Winthrop. While we were at dinner John Barney burst into the chamber, rushed up to General Scott and told him, with groans, that the President wished to see him ; that the great gun on board the Princeton had burst and killed the Secretary of State, Upshur ; the Secretary of the Navy, T. W. Gilmer ; Captain Beverly Kennon, Virgil Maxey, a Colonel Gardiner, of New York, a colored servant of the President, and desperately wounded several of the crew."

So tragic an introduction was not needed to direct public attention to the Princeton. Ericsson had placed the United States at the head of

naval powers in the application of steam-power
to warfare. He had made the experiment of the
Princeton at a great cost to himself, and two
years of concentrated effort had been devoted
to the service of the Government. For his
time, labor, and necessary expenditures he rendered a bill of $15,000, leaving the question of
what, if anything, should be charged for his
patent rights entirely to the discretion and generosity of the Government. The bill was refused
payment by the Navy Department because of
its limited discretion. Ericsson went to Congress with it, but a dozen years passed without
the slightest progress toward a settlement. A
court of claims rendered a unanimous decree in
his favor, but Congress, to which the bill was
again sent, failed to make an appropriation, and
there the matter has remained, notwithstanding
the brilliant services since rendered to this country by the inventor.

Various nations claim the invention of the
screw as applied to boats. At Triest and at
Vienna stand statues erected to Joseph Ressel,
for whom the Austrians lay claim. Commodore
Stevens, of New Jersey, is also said by Professor
Thurston to have built and worked a screw-pro-
peller on the Hudson in 1812. Whatever may
be the final decision as to Ericsson's claim in
this matter, there can be no doubt as to the
value of the services he rendered in building the
Monitor. The suggestion of the Monitor was
first made in a communication from Ericsson to
Napoleon III., dated New York, September,

1854. This paper contained a description of an iron-clad vessel surmounted by a cupola substantially as in the Monitor as finally built. The emperor, through General Favre, acknowledged the communication. Favre wrote: "The emperor has himself examined with the greatest care the new system of naval attack which you have communicated to him. His Majesty charges me with the honor of informing you that he has found your ideas very ingenious and worthy of the celebrated name of their author." For eight years Ericsson continued working upon his idea of a revolving cupola or turret upon an iron-clad raft, but found no opportunity to test the practical value of the device. His time finally came when, in 1861, the Navy Department appointed a board to examine plans for iron-clads. The board consisted of Commodores Joseph Smith, Hiram Paulding, and Charles H. Davis. Ericsson, having learned to distrust his own powers as a business agent, engaged the assistance of C. S. Bushnell, a Connecticut man of some wealth, who went to Washington and presented the designs of the Monitor to the board.

Colonel W. C. Church, Ericsson's biographer, who has just been honored by Sweden for his publications upon the life of the inventor, tells an interesting story of the negotiations concerning the vessel which was to render such signal services to the country. Bushnell could make no headway with the board and decided that Ericsson's presence in Washington was necessary. But the inventor was then, as during his whole life, averse to any self-advertisement, and preferred his workshop to any place on earth. But as he possessed a sort of rude eloquence due to enthusiasm, Bushnell got him to Washington by subterfuge. He was told that the board approved his plans for an iron-clad and that it would be necessary for him to go to the capital and complete the contract. Presenting himself before the board, what was his astonishment to find that he was not only an unexpected but apparently an unwelcome visitor. He was not long in doubt as to the meaning of this reception. To his indignation and astonishment he was informed that the plan of a vessel submitted by him had already been rejected. His first impulse was to withdraw at once. Mastering his anger, however, he inquired the reason for this decision. Commodore Smith explained that the vessel had not sufficient stability; in other words, it would be liable to upset. Captain Ericsson was too experienced a naval designer to have overlooked this point, and in a lucid explanation put his views before the board, winding up with the declaration: "Gentlemen, after what I have said, I consider it to be your duty to the country to give me an order to build the vessel before I leave this room."

Withdrawing to a corner the board held a consultation and invited the inventor to call again at one o'clock. When Ericsson returned he brought with him a diagram illustrating more fully his reasons for considering his proposed vessel to be perfectly stable. Commodore, after-

ward Admiral, Paulding was convinced, and admitted that Ericsson had taught him much about
the stability of vessels. Secretary Welles was
informed that the board reported favorably upon
Ericsson's plan, and told the inventor that he
might return to New York and begin work, as
the contract would follow him. When the con-

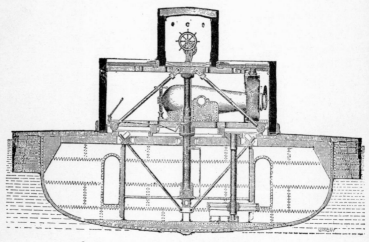

Sectional View of Monitor through Turret and Pilot-house.

tract came it was found to be a singularly one-
sided affair. If the Monitor proved vulnerable
—in other words, if it was not a success—the
money paid for it by the Navy Department was
to be refunded.

It took one hundred days to build the Monitor.
During those three months Ericsson scarcely
slept, and even in his dreams he went over the
details of the new-fangled war-engine he was

building. He named her Monitor because, he
said, she would warn the
nations of the world that
a new era in naval warfare
had begun. The story of
his untiring activity has
been told almost as often
as that of the battle be-
tween the Monitor and
the Merrimac. He was at
the ship-yard before any
of the workmen, and was
the last to leave. In the
construction of so novel a
craft difficulties of a puz-
zling nature came up every
day. If Ericsson could not
solve them on the spot, he
studied the matter in the
quiet of the night, and was
ready with his drawings
in the morning. The re-
sult of the naval battle in
Hampton Roads, on the
9th of March, 1862, be-
tween the little Monitor
and the big Merrimac
made Ericsson the hero of
the hour. Had no David
appeared to stop the rav-
ages of the Confederate

The Original Monitor.

Goliath, it is hard to say what might not have
been the injury inflicted upon the cause of the

Union by the terrible Merrimac. The United States Navy was virtually panic-stricken when the Monitor, this "Yankee cheese-box on a plank," as the Southerners called her, came to the rescue.

Notwithstanding the tremendous service rendered the country, Ericsson declined to receive more compensation for the Monitor than his contract called for. In reply to a resolution of the New York Chamber of Commerce calling for "a suitable return for his services as will evince the gratitude of the nation," Ericsson said: "All the remuneration I desire for the Monitor I get out of the construction of it. It is all-sufficient." Our grateful nation took him at his word. But honors of another and less costly kind were showered upon him. Chief Engineer Stimers, who was on the Monitor during her battle with the Merrimac, wrote to Ericsson: "I congratulate you on your great success. Thousands have this day blessed you. I have heard whole crews cheer you. Every man feels that you have saved this place to the nation by furnishing us with the means to whip an iron-clad frigate that was, until our arrival, having it all her own way with our most powerful vessels."

War vessels upon the plan of the Monitor speedily appeared among the navies of several nations. England refused at first to admit the value of the invention and was not converted until the double-turreted Miantonomoh visited her waters in 1866, when one of the London papers

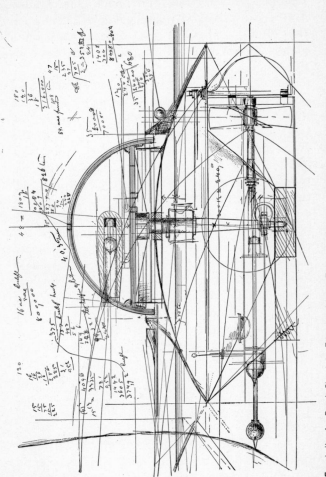

Fac-simile of a Pencil Sketch by Ericsson, giving a Transverse Section of his Original Monitor Plan, with a Longitudinal Section drawn over it.

described her appearance among the British fleet as that of a wolf among a flock of sheep. The day of the big wooden war-vessels was over. It was, nevertheless, an Englishman and a naval of-

Interior of the Destroyer, Looking toward the Bow.

ficer, Captain Cowper Coles, who sought to deprive Ericsson of the honor of his invention. Coles declared that he had devised a ship during the Crimean war, in which a turret or cupola was to protect the guns. Ericsson's letter to

Napoleon III., written in 1854, is sufficient answer to this, besides which Ericsson's scheme includes more than a stationary shield for the guns, which is all that Coles claimed. Coles succeeded, however, in inducing the British Admiralty to build a vessel according to his plans. This ill-fated craft upset off Cape Finisterre on the night of September 6, 1870, and went to the bottom with Coles and a crew of nearly five hundred men.

Having devised an apparatus that made wooden war-vessels useless, Ericsson turned his attention to the destruction of iron-clads, and devoted ten years of his life to the construction of his famous torpedo-boat, the Destroyer, upon which he spent about all the money he amassed by other work. According to his belief, no vessel afloat could escape annihilation in a battle with his Destroyer. This vessel is designed to run at sufficient speed to overtake any of the iron-clads. It offers small surface to the shot of an enemy, and besides being heavily armored, it can be partly submerged beneath the waves. When within fighting distance it fires under water, by compressed air, a projectile containing dynamite sufficient to raise a big war-ship out of the water. The explosion takes place when the projectile meets with resistance, such as the sides of a ship. To Ericsson's great disappointment, the United States Government persistently refused to purchase the Destroyer or to commission Ericsson to build more vessels of her type.

Of Ericsson's home life there is not much to be told. He was utterly wrapped up in his work.

With his devoted secretary, Mr. Arthur Taylor, his days knew scarcely any variation. Of social recreation he had none. In conversation he was

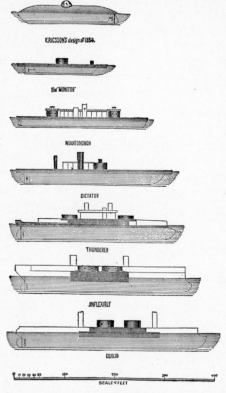

ERICSSON'S design of 1854.

the "MONITOR"

MIANTONOMOH

DICTATOR

THUNDERER

INFLEXIBLE

DUILIO

SCALE OF FEET

Development of the Monitor Idea.

abrupt and somewhat peculiar, apparently regarding all other talk than that relating to mechanics and germane subjects as a waste of words. His shrewd face, with its blue eyes and fringe of white hair, was not an unkindly one, however, and the few workmen he employed in the Beach Street house were devoted to him. No great man was ever more intensely averse to personal notoriety. Although often advised to make his Destroyer better known by means of newspaper articles, he persistently refused to see newspaper men ; and the professional interviewer and lion-hunter were his pet aversions. It was perhaps to avoid them that he left his house only after nightfall, and then but for a walk in the neighborhood.

His time was divided according to rule. For thirty years he was called by his servant at seven o'clock in the morning, and took a bath of very cold water, ice being added to it in summer. After some gymnastic exercises came breakfast at nine o'clock, always of eggs, tea, and brown bread. His second and last meal of the day, dinner, never varied from chops or steak, some vegetables, and tea and brown bread again. Ice-water was the only luxury that he indulged in. He used tobacco in no form. During the day-time he was accustomed to work at his desk or drawing-table for about ten hours. After dinner he resumed work until ten, when he started out for the stroll of an hour or more, which always ended his day. The last desk work accomplished every day was to make a record in his diary, always exactly one page long. This diary is in Swedish and comprises more than fourteen thousand pages, thus covering a period of forty years, during which he omitted but twenty days, in 1856, when he had a finger crushed by machinery. He scarcely knew what sickness was, and just before his death said that he had not missed a meal for fifteen years. He was a widower and left no children. He died in the Beach Street house, after a short illness, on March 8, 1889, and his remains were transferred to Sweden with naval honors.

The Room in which Ericsson Worked for More than Twenty Years.

Cyrus Hall McCormick.

VIII.

CYRUS HALL McCORMICK.

In the course of an argument before the Commissioner of Patents, in 1859, the late Reverdy Johnson declared that the McCormick reaper was worth $55,000,000 a year to this country, an estimate that was not disputed. At about the same time the late William H. Seward said that "owing to Mr. McCormick's invention the line of civilization moves westward thirty miles each year." Already the London *Times*, after ridiculing the McCormick reaper exhibited at the London World's Fair of 1851, as "a cross between an Astley (circus) chariot, a wheelbarrow, and a flying-machine," confessed, when the reaper had been tested in the fields, that it was "worth to the farmers of England the whole cost of this exhibition." Writing of this glorious success, Mr. Seward said: "So the reaper of 1831, as improved in 1845, achieved for its inventor a triumph which all then felt and acknowledged was not more a personal one than it was a national one. It was justly so regarded. No general or consul, drawn in a chariot through the streets of Rome by order of the Senate, ever conferred upon mankind benefits so great as he who thus vindicated the genius of our country at the World's Exhibition of Art in the metropolis of the British empire in 1851." In 1861, though declining to extend the patent for the reaper, the Commissioner of Patents, D. P. Holloway, paid the inventor this remarkable tribute : " Cyrus H. McCormick is an inventor whose fame, while he is yet living, has spread through the world. His genius has done honor to his own country, and has been the admiration of foreign nations, and he will live in the grateful recollection of mankind as long as the reaping-machine is employed in gathering the harvest." Nevertheless the extension of the patent of 1834, which act of justice would have given the inventor an opportunity to obtain an adequate reward for his work, was refused upon the extraordinary ground that " the reaper was of too great value to the public to be controlled by any individual." In other words, the benefit conferred by McCormick upon the country was too great to be paid for; therefore no effort should be made to pay for it. Finally, the French Academy of Sciences, when McCormick was elected to the Institute of France—an honor paid but to few Americans —mentioned the election as due to " his having done more for the cause of agriculture than any other living man."

It is thus evident that the tremendous service done to the civilized world by the invention of the McCormick reaper was appreciated years ago. Yet it is improbable that the whole value of the invention was fully realized. To-day the McCormick works at Chicago turn out yearly, and have turned out for several years, more than one hundred thousand reapers and mowers. At a moderate estimate every McCormick reaper, and every reaper founded upon it and containing its essential features, saves the labor of six men during the ten harvest days of the year. The

Farm where Cyrus H. McCormick was Born and Raised.

present number of reapers in operation to-day, all of them based upon the McCormick patents, is estimated at about two million, so that, counting a man's labor at $1 a day, here is a yearly saving of more than $100,000,000. The reaper thus stands beside the steam-engine and the sewing-machine as one of the most important labor-saving inventions of our time, relieving

14

millions of men from the most arduous drudg-
ery and increasing the world's wealth by hundreds of millions of dollars every year. It is
some satisfaction to know that the inventor of
the reaper lived to enjoy the fruits of his work.
A remarkable man in every respect, his ingenuity, perseverance, courage under injustice,
and generosity finally won him not only the
material rewards that were his by right, but the
esteem and honor of the civilized world.

Like Fulton and Morse, Cyrus Hall McCormick came of Scotch-Irish blood, a race marked
by fixed purpose, untiring industry in carrying
out that purpose, a strong sense of moral obligation, and an unswerving determination to do
right by the light of conscience though the heavens fall. He was born on the 15th of February,
1809, at Walnut Grove, in Rockbridge County,
Va., and was the eldest of eight children, six of
whom lived to grow up. His father, Robert
McCormick, in addition to farming, had workshops of considerable importance on his farm,
as well as a saw-mill and grist-mill and smelting
furnaces. In these workshops young Cyrus
McCormick probably got his first love for mechanical devices. Robert McCormick was an
inventor of no mean attainment. He devised
and built a thresher, a hemp-breaker, some mill
improvements, and in 1816 he made and tried
a mechanical reaper. In those days so much of
the farmer's hard labor was expended in swinging the scythe that it seems strange we have
no record of more attempts to make a machine

do the work. A schoolmaster named Ogle is said to have built a reaper in 1822, but, according to his own admission, it would not work. Bell, a Scotch minister, also contrived a reaping-machine that was tried in 1828. In the course of the subsequent patent litigation over the reaper the claims of these early inventors were made the most of by McCormick's opponents, but the courts of last resort invariably settled the question in McCormick's favor.

As a farmer boy, young Cyrus McCormick began his day's work in the fields at five o'clock. In winter he went to the Old Field School. During his boyhood he would watch his father's experiments and disappointments. His first attempt in the same direction was the construction, at the age of fifteen, of a harvesting-cradle by which he was enabled to keep up with an able-bodied workman. His first patented invention (1831) was a plough which threw alternate furrows on either side, being thus either a right-hand or left-hand plough. This was superseded in 1833 by an improved plough, also by McCormick, called the self-sharpening plough, which did excellent work. His father having worked long and unsuccessfully at a mechanical reaper, it was natural that young McCormick's mind should turn over the same problem from time to time, and his father's failures did not deter him, although Robert McCormick had suffered so much in mind and pocket through the impracticability of his reaper that he warned his son against wasting more time and money upon the dream.

One martyr to mechanical progress was enough for the McCormick family. But the possibility of making a machine do the hard, hot work of the harvest-field had a fascination for the young man, and the more he studied the discarded reaping-machine made by his father in 1816, the more firmly he became convinced that while the

Exterior of the Blacksmith Shop where the First Reaper was Built.

principle of that device was wrong, the work could be done. In those days the development of the country really depended upon some better, cheaper way of harvesting. The land was fertile, and there was practically no end of it. But labor was scarce.

Cyrus McCormick's plough was a success that encouraged him to take hold of the more difficult problem of the reaper. He found that some device, such as his father's, would cut grain after a fashion, provided it was in perfect condition and stood up straight; the moment it became matted and tangled and beaten down by wind and rain the machine was useless. Other devices had been arranged whereby a fly-wheel armed with sickles slashed off the heads of the wheat, leaving the stalks; but here again such a machine would work only when the field was in prime condition. He determined that no device was of any value which would not cut grain as it might happen to stand, stalk and all. After months of labor in his father's shop, making every part of the machine himself, in both wood and iron, as he said, he turned out, in 1831, the first reaper that really cut an average field of wheat satisfactorily. Its three great essential features were those of the reaper of to-day—a vibrating cutting-blade, a reel to bring the grain within reach of the blade, a platform to receive the falling grain, and a divider to separate the grain to be cut from that to be left standing. This machine, drawn by horses, was tested in a field of six acres of oats, belonging to John Steele, within a mile of Walnut Grove. Its work astonished the neighboring farmers who gathered to witness the test. The problem of cutting standing grain by machinery had been solved.

There were, however, certain defects in the reaper which caused Cyrus McCormick not to put the machine on the market. All the cog-wheels were of wood. There was no place upon it for either the driver or the raker. The former rode on the near horse and the latter followed on foot, raking the grain from it as best he could. But it cut grain fast, and both father and son were so impressed by its possibilities as foreshadowed in even this crude affair, that for the next few years they devoted their time, money, and thoughts to it. Robert McCormick was as enthusiastic as his son, and he is rightly entitled to a share of the honor, for his invention of 1816 turned the attention of his son to the problem and pointed out the radical errors to be avoided. A year after its first trial, with certain improvements, the reaper cut fifty acres of wheat in so perfect and rapid a manner as to insure its practical value beyond all doubt. The self-restraint shown by McCormick in refusing to sell machines until he was satisfied with them shows the man. The patent was granted in 1834, but for six years he kept at work experimenting, changing, improving, during the short periods of each harvest. In a letter to the Commissioner of Patents, on file in the Patent Office, Mr. McCormick said : " From the experiment of 1831 until the harvest of 1840 I did not sell a reaper, although during that time I had many exhibitions of it, for experience proved to me that it was best for the public as well as for myself that no sales were made, as defects presented themselves that would render the reaper unprofitable in other hands. Many improvements were found necessary, requiring a great deal of thought and study. I was sometimes flattered, at other times discouraged, and at all times deemed it best not to attempt the sale of machines until satisfied that the reaper would succeed."

About 1835 the McCormicks engaged in a partnership for the smelting of iron ore. The reaper, as a business pursuit, was yet in the distance, and the new iron industry offered large profits. The panic of 1837 swept away these hopes. Cyrus

Interior of the Blacksmith Shop where the First Reaper was Built.

sacrificed all he had, even the farm given him by his father, to settle his debts, and his scrupulous integrity in this matter turned disaster into blessing, for it compelled him to take up the reaper with renewed energy. With the aid of his father and of his brothers, William and Leander, he began the manufacture of the machine in the primitive workshop at Walnut Grove, turning out less than fifty machines a year, all of them made under great disadvantages. The sickles were made forty miles away, and as there were no railroads in those days, the blades, six feet long, had to be carried on horseback. Neither was it easy, when once the machines were made, to get them to market. The first consignment sent to the Western prairies, in 1844, was taken in wagons from Walnut Grove to Scottsville, then down the canal to Richmond, Va.; thence by water to New Orleans, and then up the Mississippi and Ohio Rivers to Cincinnati.

The great West, with its vast prairies, was the natural market for the reaper. Upon the small farms of the East hand labor might still suffice for the harvest; in the West, where the farms were enormous and labor scarce, it was out of the question. Realizing that while his reaper was a luxury in Virginia, it was a necessity in Ohio and Illinois, Cyrus McCormick went to Cincinnati in the autumn of 1844 and began manufacturing. At the same time he made some valuable improvements and obtained a second patent. The reaper had become known and the inventor rode on horseback through Illinois and Wisconsin, obtaining farmers' orders for reapers, which he offered to A. C. Brown, of Cincinnati, as security for payment, if he would use his workshops for manufacturing them. McCormick was enabled also to arrange with a firm in Brockport, N. Y., to make his reapers on a royalty, and this business provided the great wheat district of Central New York with machines. In 1847 and 1848 he obtained still other patents for new features of the reaper.

In 1846 he had already fixed upon Chicago as the best centre of operations for the reaper business, and at the close of the year he moved there. The next year the sale of the reapers rose to seven hundred, and more than doubled in 1849.

The First Reaper.

Having associated his two brothers, William S. and Leander J., with him, Cyrus McCormick found time to devote himself to introducing the reaper in the Old World. The American exhibit at the London World's Fair of 1851 was rather a small one, redeemed largely by the McCormick reaper, which the London *Times*, as I have already said, praised as worth to the farmers of Great Britain more than the whole cost of the exhibition. To it was awarded the grand prize, known as the council medal.

The reaper's advance in public favor was as steady on the other side of the water as here, and medals and honors were awarded McCormick at many important exhibitions. During the Paris Exposition of 1867 McCormick superintended the work of his reapers at a field trial held by the exposition authorities, and so conclusively defeated all competitors that Napoleon III., who walked after the reapers, expressed his determination to confer upon the inventor, then and there, the Cross of the Legion of Honor. At the French Exposition of 1878 the McCormick wire-binder won the grand prize. From 1850 the success of the reaper was assured. Mr. McCormick might have rested content with what had been achieved, but it was not his nature. He not only continued to bear upon his shoulders the larger share of responsibility of the rapidly growing business, but he labored persistently to add to the effectiveness of his invention.

The great fire that swept Chicago in 1871 left nothing of the already important works established by Mr. McCormick. But, as might be expected from such a man, he was a tower of strength to the city in her time of distress, and one of those to rally first from the blow and to inspire hope. Within a year, assisted by his brother Leander, he had raised from the ashes an immense establishment, which with the growth of the last few years now covers forty acres of ground. More than 2,000 men are here employed. The statistics for last year show that more than 20,000 tons of special bar-iron and steel, 2,800 tons of sheet steel, and 26,000 tons of castings were used in making the 142,000 machines sold. Ten million feet of lumber were used, chiefly in boxing and crating, as very little wood is now used in the reaper.

This is a marvellous development from the little Virginia shop of 1840, with its output of one machine a week, and the growth means far more for the country at large than might be inferred from these figures; the farmers of the world owe more to the McCormick reaper than they can repay. The whir of the American reaper is heard around the world. In Egypt, Russia, India, Australia the machine is helping man with more than a giant's strength. Recent American travellers through Persia have described the singular effect produced upon them by seeing the McCormick reaper doing its steady work in the fields over which Haroun Al Raschid may have roamed. And this wonderful machine is followed with awe by the more ignorant of the natives, who look upon its achievements as little short of magical. They are not far wrong, however, for it is more amazing than any wonder described in their "Arabian Nights."

The last years of Cyrus H. McCormick's life were such as have fallen to few of the world's benefactors, for as a rule the pioneer who shows the road has a hard time of it, even unto the end. Mr. McCormick had the satisfaction of

knowing not only that by his invention he had
conferred a blessing upon the workmen of the
world, but that the world had acknowledged the
debt.   Material prosperity, however, was not
considered any reason for luxurious idleness.
To the close of his life Mr. McCormick continued to supervise the business of his firm and
to make the reaper more perfect.   No great exhibition abroad or in this country passed without
some of its honors falling to the share of the
McCormick reaper.

The private life of Cyrus H. McCormick was
a happy one, and to this may be attributed no
small share of the elasticity and courage that
recognized no defeat as final.   Congress failed
to do him justice; his business was attacked by
hordes of rivals; it was interrupted by the fire of
1871 and afterward threatened by labor strikes
incited by self-seeking demagogues.   Hard work
was the rule of his life and not the exception.
But that his nature remained sweet and just is
shown by his untiring work upon behalf of others.   His home life, as I have just remarked,
was unusually blessed.   In 1858 he married Miss
Nettie Fowler, a daughter of Melzar Fowler, of
Jefferson County, New York.   Of the seven children born of this marriage, five lived to grow up,
his son, Cyrus H. McCormick, now occupying
his father's place at the head of the great works
in Chicago.   One of the daughters, Anita, is the
widow of Emmons Blaine.   The inventor of the
reaping-machine died on the 13th of May, 1884.
Robert H. Parkinson, of Cincinnati, speaks as

follows of one of the last interviews he had with Mr. McCormick: "Though struggling with the infirmities of age, he took on a kind of majesty which belongs alone to that combination of great mental and moral strength, and he surprised me by the power with which he grappled the matters under discussion, and the strong personality before which obstacles went down as swiftly and inevitably as grain before the knife of his machine. I think myself fortunate in having had this glimpse of him and in being able to remember with so much personal association a life so complete in its achievements, so far-reaching in its impress, alike upon the material, moral, and religious progress of the country, and so thoroughly successful and beneficial in every department of activity and influence which it entered." One of his friends, speaking of Mr. McCormick, said: "That which gave intensity to his purpose, strength to his will, and nerved him with perseverance that never failed was his supreme regard for justice, his worshipful reverence for the true and right. The thoroughness of his conviction that justice must be done, that right must be maintained, made him insensible to reproach and impatient of delay. I do not wonder that his character was strong, nor that his purpose was invincible, nor that his plans were crowned with an ultimate and signal success, for where conviction of right is the motive-power and the attainment of justice the end in view, with faith in God there is no such word as fail."

Cyrus H. McCormick was not only the inventor of a great labor-saving device, but he helped his fellow-man in other ways. Philanthropy, religion, education, journalism, and politics received a share of his attention. More than thirty years ago he was already an active power for good in the councils of his church. In 1859 he proposed to the General Assembly of the Presbyterian Church to endow with $100,000 the professorships of a theological seminary, to be established in Chicago. This was done, and during his lifetime he gave about half a million dollars to this institution—the Theological Seminary of the Northwest. The McCormick professorship of natural philosophy in the Washington and Lee University of Virginia, and gifts to the Union Theological Seminary at Hampden-Sidney, and to the college at Hastings, Neb., also attest his solicitude for the church in which he had been reared and of which he had been a member since 1834. In 1872 he came to the aid of the struggling organ of the Presbyterian Church in the Northwest, the *Interior*, and used it to foster union between the Old and the New Schools in the church, to aid in harmonizing the Presbyterian Church in the North and South, to advance the interests of the Theological Seminary, and to promote the welfare of the Presbyterian Church in the Northwest. Under his care and advice the *Interior* grew to be a mighty voice, expressing the convictions, the aspirations, and hopes of a great church.

Thomas A. Edison.

IX.

THOMAS A. EDISON.

THOMAS A. EDISON is sometimes spoken of
rather as a master mechanic than as a master inventor or discoverer, and with regard to some of
his work—I might even say most of it—this
characterization holds true. Edison's fame is
chiefly associated in the popular mind with the
electric light. Yet it is perfectly well known to
every student of the matter, that in all that he
has done toward making the electric light a useful every-day—or perhaps I should say every-
night—affair, he has simply made practicable
what other men had invented or discovered before him. The fundamental discovery upon
which the incandescent electric lamp is founded
—that a wire of metal or other substance if
heated to incandescence in a glass bulb from
which the air has been exhausted will give light
for a longer or shorter time, according to the
character of the apparatus and the degree to
which a perfect vacuum has been effected in
the bulb—this dates from the first half of the
century. As early as 1849 Despretz, the French
scientist, described a series of experiments with
sticks of carbon sealed in a glass globe from
which air had been exhausted. When a power-

ful current was passed through the carbon
filament it became luminous and remained so for
a short time. This was, perhaps, the first of a
long line of similar experiments
in which a number of American
physicists—Farmer, Draper,
Henry, Morse, and Maxim
among them — took part. But
notwithstanding the labors of a
score of experts in Europe and
this country, the incandescent
electric light—the wire in a glass
bulb exhausted of its air — remained a laboratory curiosity
up to the time, fifteen years ago,
when Edison took hold of it. It
gave light only for a short time
and was too expensive a toy for practical use.
The carbon burned out or disintegrated, and
the lamp failed. Edison took hold of the mechanical difficulties of the problem. With a patience,
an ingenuity, a fertility of device in which he
stands alone, he got to the bottom of each radical
defect and remedied it. The lamp would not
burn long because the platinum wire used gave
out, partly because platinum was not fitted for the
work, fusing at too low a temperature. Edison
substituted carbonized strips of paper. These
in turn failed, and he found a species of bamboo
that answered. The lamp would not burn because air still remained in the little bulbs notwithstanding the most careful manipulation with
Sprengel pumps to exhaust the air. Edison in-

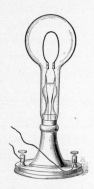

Edison's Paper Carbon
Lamp.

vented new pumps and devices by which the air, down to one millionth part, was excluded. The lamp cost too much to operate, because large copper wires were needed ·to carry the current, and the generators used up steam power too fast. Edison devised new forms of conductors and generators. All such work called more for mechanical ingenuity than for actual invention. No new principles were involved—merely the better adaptation of known methods. Given a perfect carbon, a globe perfectly free from air, cheap electric current, and cheap means of carrying it from the generating machine to the lamps, and the problem was solved.

Edison, as a master mechanic, furnished all this, or at least so nearly solved the problem as to entitle him to claim credit for having given the electric light to the world—a better illuminant than gas in every way, and destined some day to be infinitely cheaper.

With regard to Edison's work upon the telegraph, telephone, electric railway, dynamo, the ore-extracting machines, the electric pen, and a score of other inventions which have made him the most profitable customer of the United States Patent Office in this or any other generation, the labor of this remarkable genius has also been largely that of one who made practical and useful the dreams of others. And I am by no means sure that the man who does this is not entitled to more credit than he who simply suggests that such and such a wonder might be accomplished and stops there. It is certain that before

15

Edison we had no electric lights; now we have them in every important building in the country, and ere long shall have them everywhere.

Edison dislikes intensely the term discoverer as applied to himself. "Discovery is not invention," he once remarked in the course of an interesting talk with Mr. George Parsons Lathrop, printed in *Harper's Magazine*. "A discovery is more or less in the nature of an accident. A man walks along the road intending to catch the train. On the way his foot kicks against something, and looking down to see what he has hit, he sees a gold bracelet embedded in the dust. He has discovered that, certainly not invented it. He did not set out to find a bracelet, yet the value of it is just as great to him at the moment as if, after long years of study, he had invented a machine for making a gold bracelet out of common road metal. Goodyear discovered the way to make hard rubber. He was at work experimenting with india-rubber, and quite by chance he hit upon a process which hardened it —the last result in the world that he wished or expected to attain. In a discovery there must be an element of the accidental, and an important one, too; while an invention is purely deductive. In my own case but few, and those the least important, of my inventions owed anything to accident. Most of them have been hammered out after long and patient labor, and are the result of countless experiments all directed toward attaining some well-defined object. All mechanical improvements may safely be said to be in-

ventions and not discoveries. The sewing-machine was an invention. So were the steam-
engine and the typewriter. Speaking of this
latter, did I ever tell you that I made the first
twelve typewriters at my old factory in Railroad
Avenue, Newark? This was in 1869 or 1870, and
I myself had worked at a machine of similar

Edison Listening to his Phonograph.

character, but never found time to develop it
fully."

There is one great invention, however, for
which Edison deserves credit, both as discoverer
and practical inventor—the phonograph. Here
was a genuine discovery. The phonograph
knows no other parent than Edison, and he has
brought it to its present condition by devotion
and tireless skill. I have always believed in the
phonograph as an instrument destined to play

some day an important part among the blessings that ingenuity has given to man. There are still obstacles in the way of its practical success, but that the missing screw or spring—perhaps no more than that—will be found in the near future, is not doubted by any competent observer.

Thomas Alva Edison was born February 11, 1847, at Milan, Erie County, O., an obscure canal village. When a small boy, his family, a most humble one (his father being a village jack-of-all-trades, living upon odd jobs done for neighboring farmers), moved to Port Huron, Mich., where Edison's boyhood was passed. There his father was in turn tailor, well-digger, nurseryman, dealer in grain, lumber, and farm lands. His parents were of Dutch-Scotch descent and gave him the iron constitution that enables him to-day, at the age of forty-seven, to tire out the most robust of his assistants. One of his ancestors lived to the age of one hundred and two, and another to the age of one hundred and three, so that we may reasonably expect the famous inventor to open the door for us to still other wonders of which we do not yet even dream. His mother, born in Massachusetts, had a good education and at one time taught school in Canada. Of regular schooling, young Edison had but two months in his life. Whatever else he knew as a boy he learned from his mother. There are no records showing extraordinary promise on his part. He was an omniverous reader, having an intense curiosity about the world and its great men. At ten years of age he was reading

Hume's " England," Gibbon's " Rome," the Penny Encyclopædia, and some books on chemistry.

At the age of twelve he entered upon his life work as newsboy on the Grand Trunk Railroad of Canada and the Michigan Central, selling papers, books, candies, etc., to the passengers.

" Were you one of the train-boys," he was once asked, " who sold figs in boxes with bottoms half an inch thick?"

" If I recollect aright," he replied, with a merry twinkle, " the bottoms of my boxes were a good inch."

Perhaps the twelve-year-old boy learned something from the books and papers he sold. At all events he says that the love of chemistry, even at that age, led him to make the corner of the baggage-car where he stored his wares a small laboratory, fitted up with such retorts and bottles as he could pick up in the railroad workshops. He had a copy of Fresenius's " Qualitative Analysis," into which he plunged with the ardor a small boy usually shows for nothing literary unless it has a yellow cover decorated with an Indian's head. He seems also to have had a habit of " hanging around" all interesting places, from a machine-shop to a printing-office, keeping his eyes very wide open. In one such expedition he received as a gift from W. F. Storey, of the *Detroit Free Press*, three hundred pounds of old type thrown out as useless. With an old hand-press he began printing a paper of his own, the *Grand Trunk Herald*, of which he sold several hundred copies a week, the employees of the road being his best customers. " My news," he says, talking of this time, " was purely local. But I was proud of my newspaper and looked upon

From Edison's Newspaper, the "Grand Trunk Herald."

myself as a full-fledged newspaper man. My items used to run about like this : 'John Robinson, baggage-master at James's Creek Station, fell off the platform yesterday and hurt his leg.

The boys are sorry for John.' Or, ' No. 3 Burlington engine has gone into the shed for repairs.' "

This was Edison's only dip into a literary occupation. He has no predilection in that way. He realizes the value of newspapers and books, but chiefly as tools, and his splendid library at the Orange laboratory, kept with scrupulous system, is filled with scientific books and periodicals only. Telegraphy was to be the field in which he was to win his first laurels. Some years ago he told the story as follows :

" At the beginning of the civil war I was slaving late and early at selling papers; but, to tell the truth, I was not making a fortune. I worked on so small a margin that I had to be mighty careful not to overload myself with papers that I could not sell. On the other hand, I could not afford to carry so few that I should find myself sold out long before the end of the trip. To enable myself to hit the happy mean, I formed a plan which turned out admirably. I made a friend of one of the compositors of the *Free Press* office, and persuaded him to show me every day a ' galley-proof ' of the most important news article. From a study of its head-lines I soon learned to gauge the value of the day's news and its selling capacity, so that I could form a tolerably correct estimate of the number of papers I should need. As a rule I could dispose of about two hundred ; but if there was any special news from the seat of war, the sale ran up to three hundred or over. Well, one day my compositor brought me a proof-slip of which nearly the whole was taken up with a gigantic display head. It was the first report of the battle of Pittsburgh Landing—afterward called Shiloh, you know— and it gave the number of killed and wounded as sixty thousand men.

" I grasped the situation at once. Here was a chance for enormous sales, if only the people along the line could know what had happened! If only they could see the proof-slip I was then reading! Suddenly an idea occurred to me. I rushed off to the telegraph-operator and gravely made a proposition to him which he received just as gravely. He on his part was to wire to each of the principal stations on our route, asking the station-master to chalk up on the bulletin-board— used for announcing the time of arrival and de- parture of trains—the news of the great battle, with its accompanying slaughter. This he was to do at once, while I, in return, agreed to sup- ply him with current literature ' free, gratis, for nothing ' during the next six months from that date.

" This bargain struck, I began to bethink me how I was to get enough papers to make the grand *coup* I intended. I had very little cash and, I feared, still less credit. I went to the su- perintendent of the delivery department, and preferred a modest request for one thousand copies of the *Free Press* on trust. I was not much surprised when my request was curtly and gruffly refused. In those days, though, I was a pretty cheeky boy and I felt desperate, for I saw a small fortune in prospect if my telegraph operator had kept his word—a point on which I was still a trifle doubtful. Nerving myself for a great stroke, I marched upstairs into the office of Wilbur F. Storey himself and asked to see him. A few minutes later I was shown in to him. I told who I was, and that I wanted fifteen hundred copies of the paper on credit. The tall, thin, dark-eyed, ascetic-looking man stared at me for a moment and then scratched a few words on a slip of paper. 'Take that downstairs,' said he, 'and you will get what you want.' And so I did. Then I felt happier than I have ever felt since.

"I took my fifteen hundred papers, got three boys to help me fold them, and mounted the train all agog to find out whether the telegraph operator had kept his word. At the town where our first stop was made I usually sold two papers. As the train swung into that station I looked ahead and thought there must be a riot going on. A big crowd filled the platform and as the train drew up I began to realize that they wanted my papers. Before we left I had sold a hundred or two at five cents apiece. At the next station the place was fairly black with people. I raised the 'ante' and sold three hundred papers at ten cents each. So it went on until Port Huron was reached. Then I transferred my remaining stock to the wagon which always waited for me there, hired a small boy to sit on the pile of papers in the back, so as to discount any pilfering, and sold out every paper I had at a quarter of a dollar or more per copy. I remember I passed a church full of worshippers, and stopped to yell out my news. In ten seconds there was not a soul left in meeting. All of them, including the parson, were clustered around me, bidding against each other for copies of the precious paper.

" You can understand why it struck me then that the telegraph must be about the best thing going, for it was the telegraphic notices on the bulletin-boards that had done the trick. I determined at once to become a telegraph-operator. But if it hadn't been for Wilbur F. Storey I should never have fully appreciated the wonders of electrical science."

Telegraphy became a hobby with the boy. From every operator along the road he picked up something. He strung the basement of his father's house at Port Huron with wires, and constructed a short line, using for the batteries stove-pipe wire, old bottles, nails, and zinc which urchins of the neighborhood were induced to cut out from under the stoves of their unsuspecting mothers and bring to young Edison at three cents a pound. In order to save time for his experiments, he had the habit of leaping from a train while it was going at the rate of twenty-five miles an hour, landing upon a pile of sand arranged by him for that purpose. An act of personal courage—the saving of the station-master's child at Port Clements from an advancing train—was a turning-point in his career, for the grateful father taught him telegraphing in

the regular way. Telegraphy was then in its infancy, comparatively speaking; operators were
few, and good wages could be earned by means
of much less proficiency than is now required.
Still, Edison had so little leisure at his disposal
for learning the new trade, that it took him several years to become an expert operator. Most
of his studies were carried on in the corner of
the baggage-car that served him as printing-
office, laboratory, and business headquarters.
With so many irons in the fire, mishaps were
sure to occur. Once he received a drubbing on
account of an article reflecting unpleasantly
upon some employee of the road. One day
during his absence a bottle of phosphorus upset
and set the old railroad caboose on fire, where-
upon the conductor threw out all the painfully
acquired apparatus and thrashed its owner.

Edison's first regular employment as telegraph-
operator was at Indianapolis when he was
eighteen years old. He received a small salary
for day-work in the railroad office there, and
at night he used to receive newspaper reports
for practice. The regular operator was a man
given to copious libations, who was glad enough
to sleep off their effects while Edison and a young
friend of his named Parmley did his work. " I
would sit down," says Edison, "for ten minutes,
and 'take' as much as I could from the instrument, carrying the rest in my head. Then while
I wrote out, Parmley would serve his turn at
'taking,' and so on. This worked well until they
put a new man on at the Cincinnati end. He

was one of the quickest despatchers in the business, and we soon found it was hopeless for us to try to keep up with him. Then it was that I worked out my first invention, and necessity was certainly the mother of it.

"I got two old Morse registers and arranged them in such a way that by running a strip of paper through them the dots and dashes were recorded on it by the first instrument as fast as they were delivered from the Cincinnati end, and were transmitted to us through the other instrument at any desired rate of speed. They would come in on one instrument at the rate of forty words a minute, and would be ground out of our instrument at the rate of twenty-five. Then weren't we proud! Our copy used to be so clean and beautiful that we hung it up on exhibition; and our manager used to come and gaze at it silently with a puzzled expression. He could not understand it, neither could any of the other operators; for we used to hide my impromptu automatic recorder when our toil was over. But the crash came when there was a big night's work—a Presidential vote, I think it was —and copy kept pouring in at the top rate of speed until we fell an hour and a half or two hours behind. The newspapers sent in frantic complaints, an investigation was made, and our little scheme was discovered. We couldn't use it any more.

"It was that same rude automatic recorder that indirectly led me long afterward to invent the phonograph. I'll tell you how this came about.

After thinking over the matter a great deal, I came to the point where, in 1877, I had worked out satisfactorily an instrument that would not only record telegrams by indenting a strip of paper with dots and dashes of the Morse code, but would also repeat a message any number of times at any rate of speed required. I was then experimenting with the telephone also, and my mind was filled with theories of sound vibra-

Edison's Tinfoil Phonograph—the First Practical Machine.

tions and their transmission by diaphragms. Naturally enough, the idea occurred to me: if the indentations on paper could be made to give forth again the click of the instrument, why could not the vibrations of a diaphragm be recorded and similarly reproduced? I rigged up an instrument hastily and pulled a strip of paper through it, at the same time shouting, ' Hallo'! Then the paper was pulled through again, my friend Batchelor and I listening breathlessly. We heard a distinct sound, which a strong imagination might have translated into the original ' Hallo.' That was enough to lead me to a further experiment. But Batchelor was sceptical, and bet me a barrel of apples that I couldn't make the thing go. I made a drawing of a model and took it to Mr. Kruesi, at that time engaged on piece-work for me, but now assistant general manager of our machine-shop at Schenectady. I told him it was a talking-machine. He grinned, thinking it a joke; but he set to work and soon had the model ready. I arranged some tinfoil on it, and spoke into the machine. Kruesi looked on, still grinning. But when I arranged the machine for transmission and we both heard a distinct sound from it, he nearly fell down in his fright. I was a little scared myself, I must admit. I won that barrel of apples from Batchelor, though, and was mighty glad to get it."

To go back to earlier days, the story of Edison's first years as a full-fledged operator shows that from the beginning he was more of an inventor than an operator. He was full of ideas, some of which were gratefully received. One day an ice-jam broke the cable between Port Huron, in Michigan, and Sarnia, on the Canada side, and stopped communication. The river is a mile and a half wide and was impassable. Young Edison jumped upon a locomotive and seized the valve controlling the whistle. He had the idea that the scream of the whistle might be broken into long and short notes, corresponding to the dots and dashes of the telegraphic code,

"Hallo there, Sarnia! Do you get me? Do you hear what I say?" tooted the locomotive.

No answer.

"Do you hear what I say, Sarnia?"

A third, fourth, and fifth time the message went across without response, but finally the idea was caught on the other side; answering toots came cheerfully back and the connection was recovered.

Anything connected with the difficulties of telegraphy had a fascination for him. He lost many a place because of unpardonable blunders due to his passion for improvement. At Stratford, Canada, being required to report the word "Six" every half hour to the manager to show that he was awake and on duty, he rigged up a wheel to do it for him. At Indianapolis he kept press reports waiting while he experimented with new devices for receiving them. At Louisville, in procuring some sulphuric acid at night for his experiments, he tipped over a carboy of it, ruining the handsome outfit of a banking establishment below. At Cincinnati he abandoned the office on every pretext to hasten to the Mechanics' Library to pass his day in reading.

An indication of his thirst for knowledge, and of a *naïve* ignoring of enormous difficulties, is found in a project formed by him at this time to read through the whole public library. There was no one to tell him that a summary of human knowledge may be found in a moderate number of volumes, nor to point out to him what they are. Each book was to him a part of the great

domain of knowledge, none of which he meant
to lose. He began with the solid treatises of a
dusty lower shelf and actually read, in the accomplishment of his heroic purpose, fifteen feet
along that shelf. He omitted no book and nothing in the book. The list contained Newton's
" Principia," Ure's Scientific Dictionary, and
Burton's " Anatomy of Melancholy."

At that time a message sent from New Orleans
to New York had to be taken at Memphis, re-
telegraphed to Louisville, taken down again by
the operator there, and telegraphed to another
centre, and so on till it reached New York.
Time was lost and the chance of error was increased. Edison was the first to connect New
Orleans and New York directly. It was just
after the war. He perfected an automatic re-
peater which was put on at Memphis and did
its work perfectly. The manager of the office
there, one Johnson, had a relative who was also
busy on the same problem, but Edison solved it
ahead of him and received complimentary notices from the local papers. He was discharged
without cause. He got a pass as far as Decatur
on his way home, but had to walk from there to
Nashville, a hundred and fifty miles. From
there he got a pass to Louisville, where he arrived during a sharp snow-storm, clad in a linen
duster.

It was soon after this that Edison, already
a swift and competent operator when he devoted himself to practical work, received promise of employment in the Boston office. The

weather was quite cold and his peculiar dress, topped with a slouchy broad-brimmed hat, made something of a sensation. But Edison then cared as little for dress as he does to-day. So one raw wet day a tall man with a limp, wet duster clinging to his legs, stalked into the superintendent's room, and said :

" Here I am."

The superintendent eyed him from head to foot, and said :

" Who are you ? "

" Tom Edison."

" And who on earth might Tom Edison be ? "

The young man explained that he had been ordered to report for duty at the Boston office, and was finally told to sit down in the operating-room, where his advent created much merriment. The operators guyed him loudly enough for him to hear. He didn't care. A few moments later a New York sender noted for his swiftness called up the Boston office. There was no one at liberty.

" Well," said the office chief, " let that new fellow try him." Edison sat down, and for four hours and a half wrote out messages in his peculiarly clear round hand, stuck a date and number on them and threw them on the floor for the office boy to pick up. The time he took in numbering and dating the sheets were the only seconds he was not writing out transmitted words. Faster and faster ticked the instrument, and faster and faster went Edison's fingers, until the rapidity with which the messages came tum-

16

bling on the floor attracted the attention of the other operators, who, when their work was done, gathered around to witness the spectacle. At the close of the four and a half hours' work there flashed from New York the salutation:

"Hello!"

"Hello yourself," ticked back Edison.

"Who the devil are you?" rattled into the Boston office.

"Tom Edison."

"You are the first man in the country," ticked the instrument, "that could ever take me at my fastest, and the only one who could ever sit at the other end of my wire for more than two hours and a half. I'm proud to know you."

Edison was once asked with what invention he really began his career as an inventor.

"Well," said he, in reply, "my first appearance at the Patent Office was in 1868, when I was twenty-one, with an ingenious contrivance which I called the electrical vote recorder. I had been impressed with the enormous waste of time in Congress and in the State Legislatures by the taking of votes on any motion. More than half an hour was sometimes required to count the 'Ayes' and 'Noes.' So I devised a machine somewhat on the plan of the hotel annunciator that was invented long afterward, only mine was a great deal more complex. In front of each member's desk were to have been two buttons, one for 'Aye,' the other for 'No,' and by the side of the Speaker's desk a frame with two

dials, one showing the total of 'Ayes' and the other the total of 'Noes.' When the vote was called for, each member could press the button he wished and the result would appear auto-
matically before the
Speaker, who could
glance at the dials and
announce the result.
This contrivance would
save several hours of
public time every day
in the session, and I
thought my fortune
was made. I interested
a moneyed man in the
thing and we went to-
gether to Washington,
where we soon found
the right man to get
the machine adopted.

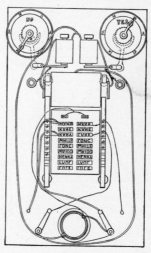

Vote Recorder—Edison's First Patented Invention.

I set forth its merits. Imagine my feelings when, in a horrified tone, he exclaimed:

"'Young man, that won't do at all. That is just what we do not want. Your invention would destroy the only hope the minority have of influencing legislation. It would deliver them over, bound hand and foot, to the majority. The present system gives them time, a weapon which is invaluable, and as the ruling majority always knows that they may some day become a minority, they will be as much averse to any change as their opponents.' I saw the force of

these remarks, and the vote recorder got no
further than the Patent Office."

But he began to believe in himself. His next
work was upon the applications of the vibratory
principle in telegraphing, upon which so many of
his subsequent inventions were founded. His
first ambitious attempt was in the direction of a
multiplex system for sending several messages
over one wire at the same time. It was not
much of a success, however, and Edison drifted
to New York, where, after a vain attempt to interest the telegraph companies in his inventions,
he established himself as an electrical expert
ready for odd jobs and making a specialty of
telegraphy. One day the Western Union Company had trouble with its Albany wire. The wire
wasn't broken, but wouldn't work, and several
days of experimenting on the part of the company's electricians only served to puzzle them
the more. As a forlorn hope they sent for
young Edison.

"How long will you give me?" he asked.
"Six hours?"

The manager laughed and told him he would
need longer than that.

Edison sat down at the instrument, established
communication with Albany by way of Pittsburgh, told the Albany office to put their best
man at the instrument, and began a rapid series
of tests with currents of all intensities. He
directed the tests from both ends, and after two
hours and a half told the company's officers that
the trouble existed at a certain point he named

on the line, and he told them what it was. They telegraphed the office nearest this point the necessary directions, and an hour later the wire was working properly. This incident first established his value in New York as an expert, and the business became profitable. Moreover, it led the different telegraph companies to give respectful attention to what he had to offer in the way of patented devices.

Edison's mechanical skill soon became so noted that he was made superintendent of the repair shop of one of the smaller telegraph companies then in existence, all of which were using what was known as the Page sounder, a device for signalling, the sole right to which was claimed by the Western Union Company. Owing to the latter company's success in a patent suit over this sounder, there came a time when an injunction was obtained, silencing all sounders of that type, and practically putting a serious obstacle in the way of rapid work. Edison was called into the president's office and the situation explained. For a long time, according to one who was present, he stood chewing vigorously upon a mouthful of tobacco, looking first at the sounder in his hand, and then falling into a brown study. At length he picked up a sheet of tin used as a " back " for manifolding on thin sheets of paper, and began to twist and cut it into queer shapes; a group of persons gathered around and watched. Not a word was spoken. Finally Edison tore off the Page sounder on the instrument before him, and substituting his bit of tin, began working.

It was not so good as the patented arrangement discarded, but it worked. In four hours a hundred such devices were in use over the line, and what would have been a ruinous interruption to business was avoided.

Edison's first large sums of money came from the sale of an improvement in the instruments used to record stock quotations in brokers' offices, commonly known as "tickers." His success in this direction led him to take a contract to manufacture some hundreds of " tickers," and his only venture in this direction was carried out with considerable success at a shop he rented in Newark about 1875. But as he told me a few years later, in talking about this incident in his career, manufacturing was not in his line. Like Thoreau, who having succeeded in making a perfect lead - pencil, declared he should never make another, he hates routine. " I was a poor manufacturer," said he, "because I could not let well enough alone. My first impulse upon taking any apparatus into my hand, from an egg-beater to an electric-motor, is to seek a way of improving it. Therefore, as soon as I have finished a machine I am anxious to take it apart again in order to make an experiment. That is a costly mania for a manufacturer."

It was his success with a device for printing stock quotations upon paper tape that finally induced several New York capitalists to accept Edison's offer to experiment with the incandescent electric light, they to pay the expense of the experiments and share in the inventions if any

Edison in his Laboratory.

were made. For the sake of quiet Edison moved out to Menlo Park, a little station on the Pennsylvania road about twenty-five miles beyond Newark, and built a shop twenty-eight feet wide, one hundred feet long, and two stories high. It was here that I first made his acquaintance, in January, 1879, soon after the newspapers had announced that he had solved the problem of the electric light. It may be remembered that gas stock tumbled in price at that time, and there was a rush to sell before the new light should displace gas altogether. One cold day I climbed the hill from the station, and once past the reception-room, in which every new-comer was carefully scrutinized, for inventors are apt to have odds and ends lying about that they do not want seen by everyone, I found myself in a long big work-shop. To anyone accustomed to the orderly appearance of the ideal machine-shop, it presented a curious appearance, for evidently half the machines in it—forges, lathes, furnaces, retorts, etc.—were dismantled for the moment and useless. Half a dozen workmen were busy in an apparently aimless manner.

Upstairs, in a room devoted to chemical experiments, I found Edison himself. He is to-day just what he was then. Prosperity has not changed him in the least, except perhaps in one particular. In those days of struggle the inventor was far less affable with visitors than he is to-day. One felt instinctively that he was a man struggling to accomplish some serious task to which he was devoting every waking thought and probably dreaming about it at night. As I strode across the laboratory in the direction indicated by one of the workmen present, a compactly built but not tall man, with rather a boyish, clean-shaven face, prematurely old, was holding a vial of some liquid up to the light. He had on a blouse such as chemists wear, but it was hardly necessary, as his clothes were well stained with acids; his hands were covered with some oil with which his hair was liberally streaked, as he had a habit of wiping his fingers upon his head. "Good clothes are wasted upon me," he once explained to me. "I feel it is wrong to wear any, and I never put on a new suit when I can help it." Edison has been slightly deaf for a number of years, and like all persons of defective hearing, closely watches anyone with whom he talks. His patience with visitors is proverbial, and provided any intelligence is shown, he will plunge into long explanations. As he goes on from point to point, warming up to his subject, he is sometimes quite oblivious to the fact that it is all lost upon his visitor until brought back by some question or comment which shows that he might as well talk Sanscrit. Then he laughs and goes back to simpler matters.

I watched him for a few moments before presenting myself. After a long look at his bottle, held up against the light, he put it down again on the table before him, and resting his head between his hands, both elbows on the table, he peered down at the bottle as if he expected it to say something. Then, after a moment's brown study, he would seize it again, give it a shake, as if to shake its secret out, and hold it up to the light. As pantomime nothing could have been more expressive. That liquid contained a secret it would not give up, but if it could be made to give it up, Edison was the man to do it, as a terrier might worry the life out of a rat.

The secret of his success might well be " Persistency, more persistency, still more persistency." One of his foremen relates that once in Newark when his printing telegraph suddenly refused to work, he locked himself into his laboratory, declaring that he would not come out till the trouble was found. It took him sixty hours, during which time his only food consisted of crackers and cheese eaten at the bench ; then he went to bed and slept twenty hours at a stretch. At another time, during the height of the first electric-light excitement, all the lamps he had burning in Menlo Park, about eighty in all, suddenly went out, one after another, without apparent cause. Everything had gone well for nearly a month and the great success of the experiment had been published to the world. If the lamps, with their carbon filaments of charred paper would burn for a month there seemed to be no reason why they should not burn for a year, and Edison was stunned by the catastrophe. The trouble was evidently in the lamps themselves, for new lamps burned well. Then began the most exciting and most exhaustive series of experiments ever undertaken by an American physicist. For five days Edison remained day and night at the laboratory, sleeping only when his assistants took his place at whatever was going on. The difficulties in the way of experimenting with the incandescent lamp are enormous because the light only burns when in a vacuum. The instant the glass is broken, out it goes. Edison's

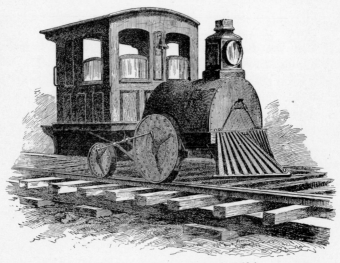

Edison's Menlo Park Electric Locomotive (1880).

eyes grew weak studying the brilliant glow of the carbon filament. At the end of the five days he took to his bed, worn out with excitement and sick with disappointment. During the last two days and nights he ate nothing. He could not sleep, for the moment he left the laboratory and closed his eyes some new test suggested itself. Neither was there much sleep for his faithful force. Ordinarily one of the most considerate of men, he seemed quite surprised when rest and refreshments were sometimes suggested as in order after fifteen hours' incessant work. The trouble was finally discovered to be one that time alone could have proved. The air was not sufficiently exhausted from the lamps. To add to the discomfiture of the inventor, a professor of physics in one of the well-known colleges declared in a newspaper article widely circulated that the Edison lamp would never last long enough to pay for itself.

"I'll make a statue of that man," said Edison to me one day when he was still groping in the dark for the secret of his temporary defeat, "and I'll illuminate it brilliantly with Edison lamps and inscribe it: 'This is the man who said the Edison lamp would not burn.'"

To go back to Edison, shaking his bottle in the sunlight, his brown study gave way to a pleasant smile of welcome when I had made my business known. "Take a look at these filings," he said, making room for me at the bench. "See how curiously they settle when I shake the bottle up. In alcohol they behave one way, but in oil in this way. Isn't that the most curious thing you ever saw—better than a play at one of your city theatres, eh?" and he chuckled to himself as he shook them up again.

"What I want to know," he went on, more to himself than to me, "is what they mean by it, and I'm going to find out." To me the interesting spectacle was Edison tossing up his bottle and watching the filings settle, and not the curious behavior of the filings.

When he put the bottle by, with a deep sigh, he took me over the whole place, pointing out with particular pride the apparatus for making the paper carbons for the lamps, and the new forms of Sprengel mercury pumps that did better work in extracting air from the lamps than any yet devised.

Looking back to that first visit to Edison, the first of perhaps a score that I have had occasion to make him in the last fifteen years, what impressed me most was the immensity of the field in which he takes an interest. Ask Edison what he thinks will be the next step in the development of the sewing-machine, or the telescope, the microscope, the steam-engine, the electric-motor, the reaping-machine, or any device by which man accomplishes much work in little time, and invariably it will be found that he has some novel ideas upon the subject, perhaps fanciful in the extreme, but practical enough to show that he has pondered the matter. He shares the opinion of the gentleman who insists that whatever is is wrong, but only to this extent: that whatever is might be better. Authority means nothing to him; he must test for himself. For instance, it is well known that he rejects the Newtonian theory in part and holds that motion is an inherent property of matter; that it pushes, finding its way in the direction of least resistance, and is not pulled or attracted. "It seems to me," he said once, "that every atom is possessed by a certain amount of primitive intelligence. Look at the thousand ways in which atoms of hydrogen combine with those of other elements, forming the most diverse substances. Do you mean to say that they do this without intelligence? Atoms in harmonious and useful relation assume beautiful or interesting shapes and colors, or give forth a pleasant perfume, as if expressing their satisfaction. In sickness, death, decomposition, or filth the disagreement of the component atoms immediately makes itself felt by bad odors." It is partly due to this belief in the sensibility of atoms that Edison attributes his faith in an intelligent Creator.

It is hard to say into what field of inquiry Edison has not dipped. He told me once that whenever he travelled he carried a note-book with him, in which he jotted down suggestions for experiments to be made. Railway journeys, at a time when Edison was a constant traveller, were productive of much material of this kind, for the inventor never sleeps when travelling, and his brain works, going over, even in a doze, the thousand and one aspects of his work, and evolving theories to be dismissed almost as soon as evolved. His mind, when at rest, reviews his day's work almost automatically, just as a chess-player's brain will, after an exciting game, go over every situation in a half dream-like condition and evolve new solutions. He has great respect for even what appear to be the most inconsequential observations, provided they are made by a competent person, and a large force in his splendid laboratory at Orange is always employed in studies that appear to the outsider

Orange N.J. Nov 15/87

Wait for 2½ weeks, then will have foreign papers filed and will give you all the information nobody else can get anything

Yours Edison

to be aimless; for instance, the action of chemicals upon various substances or upon each other. Strips of ivory in a certain oil become transparent in six weeks. A globule of mercury in water takes various shapes for the opposite poles of the electric-battery upon the addition of a little potassium. There is no present use for the knowledge of such facts, but it is recorded in voluminous note-books, and some day the connecting-link in the chain of an invaluable discovery may here be found.

My next visit to Menlo Park was a few months later, when I found Edison in bed sick with disappointment. The lamps had again taken to antics for which no remedy or explanation could be discovered. There was an air of desolation over the place. The laboratory was cold and comfortless. Upon every side were signs of strict economy. Most of the assistants were young men glad to work for little or nothing. For the last month Edison had been working in the direction of a general improvement of all parts of the lamp instead of devoting himself to one feature. Expert glass-blowers were brought to Menlo Park, the air-pumps were made more perfect, new substances were tried for carbons. All this had taken time, during which outsiders freely predicted failure. The stock in the enterprise fell to such a price that it was hard to raise money for the maintenance of the laboratory. It was argued, and with some truth, as I have had occasion to remark, that Edison had really discovered nothing new; he had attempted to do what a dozen famous men had tried before him and he had failed. The quotations of New York gas stocks rose again.

The next time I visited the laboratory, a few

days later, Edison was up again and talking cheerfully. But he had grown five years older in five months. " I shall succeed," he said to me, " but it may take me longer than I at first supposed. Everything is so new that each step is in the dark; I have to make the dynamos, the lamps, the conductors, and attend to a thousand details that the world never hears of. At the same time I have to think about the expense of my work. That galls me. My one ambition is to be able to work without regard to the expense. What I mean is, that if I want to give up a whole month of my time and that of my whole establishment to finding out why one form of a carbon filament is slightly better than another, I can do it without having to think of the cost. My greatest luxury would be a laboratory more perfect than any we have in this country. I want a splendid collection of material—every chemical, every metal, every substance in fact that may be of use to me, and I hardly know what may not be of use. I want all this right at hand, within a few feet of my own house. Give me these advantages and I shall gladly devote fifteen hours a day to solid work. I want none of the rich man's usual toys, no matter how rich I may become. I want no horses or yachts— have no time for them. I want a perfect workshop."

In the last twelve years Edison has seen his dream fulfilled. His electric light has not displaced gas, by any means, but it has been the foundation of a business large enough to make the inventor sufficiently rich to build the finest laboratory in the world, in the most curious room of which are to be found the three hundred models of machinery and apparatus of various kinds devised by Edison in the last twenty years and made by himself or under his eye. He is still a gaunt fellow, with a slight stoop, a clean-shaven face, and a low voice. His hands are still

The Home of Thomas A. Edison.

soiled with acids, his clothes are shabby, and there is always a cigar in his mouth.

The Edison laboratory deserves a chapter by itself. In 1886 Edison bought a fine villa in Llewellyn Park at a cost of $150,000. He took the house as it stood, with all its luxurious fittings, rather to please his wife than himself; a corner of the laboratory would suit him quite as well. Right outside the gates of the park and within

view of the house, he bought ten acres of land
and began his laboratory. Two handsome struct-
ures of brick, each 60 feet wide, 100 feet long,
and four stories high, accommodate the machine-
shop, library, lecture-room, experimental workshops, assistants' rooms and store-rooms. The
boiler-house and dynamo-rooms are outside the
main buildings. Also, in a separate room, the
floor of which consists of immense blocks of
stone, are the delicate instruments of precision

Edison's Laboratory.

used in testing electric currents. The instruments in this one room, twenty feet square, cost
$18,000 to make and to import from Europe.
Upon first entering the main building, the visitor finds what is apparently a busy factory of
some sort, with long rows of machinery, from
steam-hammers to diamond-lathes. Everywhere
workmen are busy at their tasks, and Edison has
good reason to be proud of his laboratory force,
for it consists of the picked workmen of the
country. Whenever he finds in one of the Edison

factories in Newark, New York, Schenectady, or elsewhere a particularly expert and intelligent man, he has him transferred to the Orange laboratory, where, at increased pay for shorter hours, the man not only finds life pleasanter, but has a chance of learning and becoming somebody. The whole place hums with the rattle of machinery and glows with electric light. There are eighty assistants, who have charge of the various departments. The most expert iron-workers, glass-blowers, wood-turners, metal-spinners, screw-makers, chemists, and machinists in the country are to be found here. A rough drawing of the most complicated model is all they require to work from.

The store-rooms contain all the material needed. Four store-keepers are employed to keep the supplies, valued at $100,000, in order and ready for use at a moment's notice. Each article is put down in a catalogue which shows the shelf or bottle where it may be found. Every known metal, every chemical known to science, every kind of glass, stone, earth, wood, fibre, paper, skin, cloth, is to be found there. In making up the chemical collection an assistant was kept at work for weeks going through the three most exhaustive works on chemistry in English, French, and German, making a note of every substance mentioned, and this list constituted the order for chemicals, an order, by the way, which it required seven months to fill. In the glass department, for instance, there is every known kind of glass, from plates two inches thick to the finest film, and if anythiny else in the way of glass is needed, the glass-workers are there to make it. This stupendous collection of material, filling one floor, is intended to guard against annoying delays that might occur at critical times for want of some rare material. In 1885, when working upon an apparatus for getting a current of electricity directly from heat —the thermo-electric generator—Edison's work was brought to a standstill for want of a few pounds of nickel, an article not then to be found in any quantity in this country. The store-room was organized to avert such delays. The library is the only part of the main building that shows any attempt at decoration. It is a superb room, 60 feet by 40, with a height of 25 feet. Galleries run around the second story. At one end is a monumental fireplace, and in the centre of the hall a fine group of palms and ferns. The room is finished in oiled hard wood and lighted by electricity. Fine rugs cover the floors. The shelves contain nothing but scientific works and the files of the forty-six scientific periodicals in English, French, and German to which Edison subscribes. They are indexed by a librarian as soon as received, so that Edison can see at a glance what they contain concerning the special fields in which he is interested.

Nothing in this big establishment, often employing more than one hundred persons, is made for sale. It is wholly devoted to experimental work and tests. Its expenses, said to be more than $150,000 a year, are paid by the commercial companies in which Edison is interested, he, on his part, giving them the benefit of any improvements made. Thus in one room hundreds of incandescent electric lamps burn night and day the year through. Each lamp is specially marked and when it burns out more quickly than the average, or lasts longer, a special study is made as to the contributing causes. It may seem impossible that the suggestions of one man can keep busy a big workshop upon experiments the year round, but Edison says that the temptation is always to increase the force. When it is remembered that the list of Edison's patents reaches to seven hundred and forty, and that on the electric light alone he has worked out several hundred theories, the wonder ceases. Ten minutes' work with a pencil may sketch an apparatus that a dozen men cannot finish inside of a fortnight.

When the new Orange laboratory was finished and Edison found himself with time and means at his disposal, his first thought was to take up his phonograph. The history of the great hopes built upon the phonograph and the bitter disappointment that followed is too familiar to need repetition here. As may be imagined, Edison is most keenly bent upon tightening the loose screw that has prevented it from doing all that its friends predicted for it. He still works at other problems, but chiefly as relaxation. He rests from inventing one thing by inventing something else.

One day recently, when I found him less con-

Library at Edison's Laboratory.

fident than usual as to the triumph of the phonograph in the near future, he said: "There are
some difficulties about the problem that seem
insurmountable. I go on smoothly until at a
certain point I run my head against a stone
wall; I cannot get under, over, or around it.
After butting my head against that wall until it
aches, I go back to the beginning again. It is
absurd to say that because I can see no possible
solution of the problem to-day, that I may not
see one to-morrow. The very fact that this century has accomplished so much in the way of
invention, makes it more than probable that the
next century will do far greater things. We
ought to be ashamed of ourselves if we are content to fold our hands and say that the telegraph, telephone, steam-engine, dynamo, and
camera having been invented, the field has been
exhausted. These inventions are so many wonderful tools with which we ought to accomplish
far greater wonders. Unless the coming gener-
ations are particularly lazy, the world ought to
possess in 1993 a dozen marvels of the usefulness
of the steam-engine and dynamo. The next step
in advance will perhaps be the discovery of a
method for transforming heat directly into electricity. That will revolutionize modern life by
making heat, power, and light almost as cheap
as air. Inventors are already feeling their way
toward this wonder. I have gone far enough on
that road to know that there are several stone
walls ahead. But the problem is one of the most
fascinating in view."

X.

ALEXANDER GRAHAM BELL.

SIR CHARLES WHEATSTONE, the eminent English electrician, while engaged in perfecting his system of telegraphy discovered that wires charged with electricity often carried noises in a curious manner. He made and exhibited at the Royal Society, in 1840, a clock in which the tick of another clock miles away was conveyed through a wire. This experiment appears to have been one of the germs of the telephone. In 1844 Captain John Taylor, also an Englishman, invented an instrument to which he gave the name of the telephone, but it had nothing electrical about it. It was an apparatus for conveying sounds at sea by means of compressed air forced through trumpets. He could make his telephone heard six miles away. The first real suggestion of the telephone as we know it comes from Reis, the German professor of physics at Friedrichsdorf, who in 1860 constructed with a coil of wire, a knitting-needle, the skin of a German sausage, the bung of a beer-barrel, and a strip of platinum an instrument which reproduced the sound of the voice by the vibration of the membrane and sent a series of clicks along an electric wire to an electro-magnetic receiver

Professor Bell Sending the First Message, by Long-distance Telephone, from New York to Chicago.

at the other end of the wire. The same idea was taken up in this country by Elisha Gray, Edison, and by Alexander Graham Bell, who first exhibited at the Centennial Exhibition an apparatus that transmitted speech by electricity in a fairly satisfactory manner. The American claimants to the honor of having invented the telephone include Daniel Drawbaugh, a back-woods genius of Pennsylvania, who claims to have made and used a practical telephone in 1867–68. A large fortune has been spent in fighting Drawbaugh's claims against the Bell monopoly, but the courts have finally decided in favor of the latter. It should be recorded as a matter of justice to Mr. Gray, that he appears to have solved the problem of conveying speech by electricity at about the same time as Bell. Both these inventors filed their caveats upon the telephone upon the same day—February 14, 1876. It was Bell's good fortune to be the first to make his device practically effective.

Alexander Graham Bell is not an American by birth. He was born in Edinburgh, Scotland, on the 1st of March, 1847. His father, Alexander Melville Bell, was the inventor of the system by which deaf people are enabled to read speech more or less correctly by observing the motion of the lips. His mother was the daughter of Samuel Symonds, a surgeon in the British navy.

In 1872 the Bells moved to Canada, and young Alexander Bell became widely known in Boston as an authority in the teaching of the deaf and dumb. He first carried to great perfection in this country the art of enabling the deaf and dumb to enunciate intelligible words and sounds that they themselves have never heard. Most of his art he acquired from his father, one of the most expert of teachers in this field. The elder Bell is still active in his work, constantly devising new methods and experiments. He lives in Washington with his son and is frequently heard in lectures in New York and Boston.

In 1873 Alexander Bell began to study the transmission of musical tones by telegraph. It was in the line of his work with deaf and dumb people to make sound vibrations visible to the eye. With the phonautograph he could obtain tracings of such vibrations upon blackened paper by means of a pencil or stylus attached to a vibrating cord or membrane. He also succeeded in obtaining tracings upon smoked glass of the vibrations of the air produced by vowel sounds. He began experimenting with an apparatus resembling the human ear, and upon the suggestion of Dr. Clarence J. Blake, the Boston aurist, he tried his work upon a prepared specimen of the ear itself. Observation upon the vibrations of the various bones within the ear led him to conceive the idea of vibrating a piece of iron in front of an electro-magnet.

Mr. Bell was at this time an instructor in phonetics, or the art of visible speech, in Monroe's School of Oratory in Boston. One of his old pupils describes him then as a swarthy, foreign-looking personage, more Italian than

English in appearance, with jet-black hair and dark skin. His manner was earnest and full of conviction. He was an enthusiast in his work, and only emerged from his habitual diffidence when called upon to talk upon his studies and views. He was miserably poor and almost without friends. When he was attacked with muscular rheumatism, in 1873, his hospital expenses were paid by his employer, and his only visitors were some of the pupils at the school.

Until the close of 1874, Bell's experiments seemed to promise nothing of practical value. But in 1875 he began to transmit vibrations between two armatures, one at each end of a wire. He was much interested at the time in multiple telegraphy and fancied that something might come of some such arrangement of many magnetic armatures responding to the vibrations set up in one.

In November, 1875, he discovered that the vibrations created in a reed by the voice could be transmitted so as to reproduce words and sounds. One day in January, 1876, he called a dozen of the pupils at Monroe's school into his room and exhibited an apparatus by which singing was more or less satisfactorily transmitted by wire from the cellar of the building to a room on the fourth floor. The exhibition created a sensation among the pupils, but, although no attempts were made by Bell to conceal what he was doing, or how he did it, the noise of his discovery does not seem to have reached the outside world. With an old cigar-box, two hundred feet of wire, two magnets from a toy fish-pond, the first Bell telephone was brought into existence. The apparatus was, however, not yet the practical telephone as we know it, but it was sufficient of a curiosity to warrant its exhibition in an improved form at the Centennial Exhibition, when Sir William Thomson spoke of it as "perhaps the greatest marvel hitherto achieved by the electric telegraph."

The next year Bell succeeded in bringing the telephone to the condition in which it became of immediate practical value. Strange to say, the public was at first slow to appreciate the great importance of the invention, and when Bell took it to England, in 1877, he could find no purchaser for half the European rights at $10,000. In this country, thanks to the business energy of Professor Gardiner Hubbard, of Harvard, Bell's father-in-law, the telephone was soon made commercially valuable, and there are now said to be nearly six hundred thousand telephones in use in the United States alone.

Professor Bell, as may be imagined, is not idle. His vast fortune has enabled him to continue costly experiments in aiding deaf and dumb people, and it will probably be in this field that his next achievement will be made. Personally, he is a reserved and thoughtful man, wholly given up to his scientific work. His wife, whom he married in 1876, was one of his deaf and dumb pupils. It is often said that it was largely due to his intense desire to soften her misfortune that his experiments were so exhaustive and finally became so productive in another direction. His home life in Washington, where he bought, in 1885, the superb house on Scott Circle known as " Broadhead's Folly," after the man who built it and ruined himself in so doing, is said to be an ideally peaceful and happy one, given up to study and efforts to alleviate the troubles of the deaf and dumb.

As in the case of most inventions of such immense value as the telephone, a fortune has had to be spent in order to protect the patent rights; but in Bell's case the inventor's money reward has been ample and is now said to amount to more than $1,000,000 a year. Just at present Mr. Bell is engaged upon a modification of the phonograph, which may enable persons not wholly deaf to hear a phonographic reproduction of the human voice, even if they cannot hear the voice itself. Honors have poured in upon him within the last fifteen years. In 1880 the French Government awarded him the Volta prize of $10,000, which Mr. Bell devoted to founding the Volta Laboratory in Washington, an institution for the use of students. In 1882 he also received from France the ribbon of the Legion of Honor.

XI.

AMERICAN INVENTORS, PAST AND PRESENT.

THERE are now in force in this country nearly three hundred thousand patents for inventions and devices of more or less importance and aid to everyone. To how great a degree the world is indebted to the inventor, very few of us realize. The more we think of the matter, however, the more are we likely to believe that the inventor is mankind's great benefactor. Watt should stand before Napoleon in the hero-worship of the age, and the man who perfected the friction-match before the author of an epic. Some day this redistribution of the world's honors will surely take place, and it should be a satisfaction to us Americans that our country stands so high in the ranks of inventive genius. Within the last half century Americans have contributed, to mention only great achievements, the telegraph, the telephone, the electric light, the sewing-machine, the reaper, and vulcanized rubber, to the world's wealth—a far larger contribution than that of any other nation. What may not the next generation produce? Some people seem to believe that so much has already been invented as to have exhausted the field. In this connection I have quoted in another place some remarks Mr. Edison once made to me as to what the next fifty years might bring forth. Still more astonishing than our past fecundity in invention would be future barrenness. This century has done its work and produced its marvels with comparatively blunt tools, or no tools at all. The next century will be able to work with superb instruments of which our grandfathers knew nothing. The school-boy to-day knows more of the forces of nature and their useful application than the magician of fifty years ago. It has been said that the fifteen blocks in the "Gem" puzzle can be arranged in more than a million different ways. The material in the game at which man daily plays is so infinitely more complex that the number of combinations cannot be written out in figures. The rôle played by invention in modern life is infinitely greater than during preceding ages. One invention, by affording a new tool, makes others possible. The steam-engine made possible the dynamo, the dynamo made possible the electric light. In its turn the electric light may lead to wonders still more extraordinary.

The degree to which invention has contributed to civilization is far from suspected by the careless observer. Almost everything we have or use is the fruit of invention. Man might be defined as the animal that invents. The air we breathe and the water we drink are provided by Nature, but we drink water from a vessel of some kind, an invention of man. Even if we drink from a shell or a gourd, we shape it to serve a new purpose. If we want our air hotter or colder, we resort to invention, and a vast amount of ingenuity has been expended upon putting air in motion by means of fans, blowers, ventilators, etc. We take but a small part of our food as animals do—in the natural state. The savage who first crushed some kernels of wheat between two stones invented flour, and we are yet hard at it inventing improvements upon his process. The earliest inventions probably had reference to the procuring and preparing of food, and the ingenuity of man is still exercised upon these problems more eagerly than ever before. During the last fifty years the power of man to produce food has increased more than during the preceding fifteen centuries. Sixty years ago a large part of the wheat and other grain raised in the world was cut, a handful at a time, with a scythe, and a man could not reap much more than a quarter of an acre a day. With a McCormick reaper a man and two horses will cut from fifteen to twenty acres of grain a day. In the threshing of grain, invention has achieved almost as much. A man with a machine will thresh ten times as much as he formerly could with a flail.

It is less than sixty years since matches have come into common use. Many old men remember the time in this country when a fire could be kindled only with the embers from another fire, as there were no such things as matches. Most of us who have reached the age of forty remember the abominable, clumsy sulphur-matches of 1860, as bulky as they were unpleasant. And yet the first sulphur-matches, made about 1830, cost ten cents a hundred. To-day the safety match, certain and odorless, is sold at one-tenth of this price. The introduction of kerosene was one of the blessings of modern life. It added several hours a day to the useful, intelligent life of man, and who can estimate the influence of these evening hours upon the advance of civilization? The evening, after the day's work is done, has been the only hour when the workingman could read. Before cheap and good lights were given him, reading was out of the question. Gas marked a step in advance, but only for large towns, and now electricity bids fair soon to displace gas; and we hear vague suggestions of a luminous ether that will flood houses with a soft glow like that of sunlight.

TOWNSEND AND DRAKE—THE INTRODUCTION OF COAL OIL.

In 1850 sperm oil, then commonly used in lamps, had become high-priced, owing to the failure of the New Bedford whalers, and cost $2.25 a gallon. Oil obtained by the distillation of coal was tried, but was also too costly— not less than $1 a gallon. It burned well, but its odor was frightful. The problem of a cheap and pleasant light was solved by James M. Townsend and E. L. Drake, both of New Haven.

18

In 1854 a man brought to Professor Silliman, of Yale, some oil from Oil Creek, Pa., to be tested. His report was so favorable that a company was formed, which leased all the land along Oil Creek upon which were traces of the new rock oil. The hard times of 1857 came before any headway had been made, and the company tried to find some way of ridding itself of the lease. At this time Townsend, who knew something about the property, undertook to get possession. Boarding in the same house in New Haven was E. L. Drake, once a conductor on the New York & New Haven Railroad, who had been obliged to give up work on account of ill-health. Townsend proposed that as Drake could get railroad passes as an ex-employee, he should go to Pennsylvania and look into the property. He did so, and reported that a fortune might be made by gathering the oil and bottling it for medicinal purposes. Drake and Townsend organized the Seneca Oil Company. The oil was gathered by digging trenches, and was sold at $1 a gallon. Drake suggested that it might be well to bore for oil. A man familiar with salt-well boring was brought from Syracuse, and in 1859 the first well was begun at Titusville under the supervision of Drake. He was commonly considered by the neighbors to be insane. The work was costly and slow. When many months and about $50,000 had been spent, the stockholders in the company refused to go any further— all except Townsend, who sent his last $500 to Drake, with instructions to use it in paying debts and his expenses in reaching home. On the day before the receipt of this money— August 29, 1859—the auger, which was down sixty-eight feet, struck a cavity, and up came a flow of oil that filled the well to within five feet of the surface. Pumping began at the rate of five hundred gallons a day, and a more powerful pump doubled this flow. As this oil was worth a dollar a gallon, fortune was within sight. But the very quantity of the oil proved to be the company's ruin. Their works were destroyed by fire in the winter of 1859–60, and before they could be rebuilt, scores of other wells, some of them requiring no pumping apparatus, had been sunk in the neighborhood. The supply was soon far in excess of the demand, which was limited by the small number of refineries, the want of good lamps in which to burn the oil, and the attacks by manufacturers of other oils. Such was the effect of these causes that the new oil fell to a dollar a barrel, a price so low that it did not pay for the handling. The Seneca Oil Company was so much discouraged that they sold out their leases and disbanded. Both Townsend and Drake would have died richer men had they never heard of the Pennsylvania rock oil.

The Clarks and the Telescope.

The fame of American telescopes is due to the work and inventions of the Clark family of Cambridgeport, Mass., the descendants of Thomas

Clark, the mate of the Mayflower. The founder of the great—in a scientific sense—house of Alvan Clark & Sons, telescope-makers, was a remarkable man. Until after his fortieth year he devoted himself to portrait-painting. In 1843 his attention was accidentally turned toward telescope-making. One day the dinner-bell at

Alvan Clark.

Phillips Academy, Andover, Mass., happened to break. The pieces were gathered up by one of Clark's boys, George, who proceeded to melt them in a crucible over the kitchen fire, declaring that he was going to make a telescope. His mother laughed, but his father was deeply interested and helped the boy make a five-inch reflecting telescope which showed the satellites of Jupiter. This was the beginning of telescope-

making in the Clark family, an industry which
has given to the scientific world its most remarkable lenses. Alvan Clark dropped his paint-
brushes, never to take them up again until at the
age of eighty-three he made an excellent portrait
of his little grandson. To Alvan G. Clark, the
present head of the house, are chiefly due the
scores of devices by which American ingenuity
has surpassed the slower European methods.
The delicacy required in the manipulation and
grinding of the immense lenses made by the
Clarks is almost incredible. The latest triumph
of the firm—a forty-inch lens for the Spence
Observatory at Los Angeles, Cal.—required two
years of grinding and polishing after a piece of
glass perfect enough had been obtained. So
delicately finished is it that half a dozen sharp
rubs with the soft part of a man's thumb would
be sufficient to ruin it. Alvan G. Clark is now a
man sixty-one years old. He has lived all his
life at the home in Cambridgeport. His greatest sorrow is that there is no son of his to carry
on the work after his death. His only son died
a few years ago, just as he was beginning to show
wonderful aptitude in the art which has made
the family famous in all the great observatories
of the world.

JOHN FITCH AND OLIVER EVANS—STEAM TRANSPORTATION.

In looking over the work done by American inventors, the great names are those to be found at the heads of the preceding chapters. But the list is by no means exhausted. Among the early men of achievement in the field of invention I have had to omit at least a dozen whose work deserves more than a paragraph. The history of the steamboat is not complete without reference to John Fitch.

Fulton was fortunate in making the first really successful attempt at propelling boats by steam, but Fitch came very near reaping the honors for this invention. The account of Fitch's life and experiments, written by himself and now in the possession of the Franklin Library of Philadelphia, clearly shows that this unhappy genius really deserves to share in Fulton's glory. Fitch was born in Connecticut, in January, 1743, more than twenty years before Fulton. He was a farmer's boy and picked up knowledge as best he could. Before he was twenty he had learned clock-making and then button-making. It was in 1788 that he obtained his first patent for a steamboat. His experimental boat was an extraordinary affair, fully described in the *Columbian* (Philadelphia) *Magazine* for December, 1786. Its motive power consisted of a clumsy engine that moved horizontal bars, upon which were fastened a number of oars or paddles. So far as possible the machine imitated the movements of a man rowing. This boat made eight miles an hour in calm water. Finding nothing but ridicule for his project here, as his steamboat cost too much money to run as a commercial undertaking, Fitch went to Europe, and was equally unsuccessful there. There is still in existence a letter from him in which he predicts that steam would some day carry vessels across the Atlantic. He died in 1796, without having contributed more than a curiosity to the art of steam navigation.

Another early inventor was Oliver Evans, who has been called the Watt of America. In 1804 Evans offered to build for the Lancaster Turnpike Company a steam-carriage to carry one hundred barrels of flour fifty miles in twenty-four hours. The offer was derided. Here is one of Evans's predictions written at about this time: " The time will come when people will travel in stages, moved by steam-engines, from one city to another, almost as fast as birds fly, fifteen or twenty miles an hour. Passing through the air with such velocity, changing the scene with such rapid succession, will be the most rapid, exhilarating exercise. A carriage (steam) will set out from Washington in the morning, the passengers will breakfast at Baltimore, dine at Philadelphia, and sup in New York the same day. To accomplish this, two sets of railways will be laid so nearly level as not in any way to deviate more than two degrees from a horizontal line, made of wood, or iron, or smooth paths of broken stone or gravel, with a rail to guide the carriages so that they may pass each other in different directions and travel by night as well as by day. Engines will drive boats ten or twelve miles per hour, and there will be many hundred steamboats running on the Mississippi." In 1805 Evans built a steam-carriage propelled by a sort of paddle-wheel at the stern, the paddles touching the ground. This apparatus he named the "Oructor Amphibolis," and it is believed to have been the first application of steam in America to the propelling of land carriages. He died in 1819 without having seen his steam-carriage come to anything practicable. He made a fortune, however, from some patents upon flour-mill improvements.

AMOS WHITTEMORE AND THOMAS BLANCHARD.

In the domain of textile fabrics Amos Whittemore, the Massachusetts inventor of the card-machine, which did away with the old-fashioned method of making cards for cotton and woollen factories, must be mentioned. Before Whittemore's machine came into use, about 1812, such cards were made by hand, the laborer sticking one by one into sheets of leather the wire staples, which operation gave work to thousands of families in New England early in the century. Whittemore made a fortune by his invention, and devoted the last years of his life to astronomy.

Another Massachusetts boy, Thomas Blanchard, invented the lathe for turning irregular objects, and well deserves mention. Born in 1788, he was noted as a boy for his efficiency in the New England accomplishment of whittling, making wonderful windmills and water-wheels with his knife. When thirteen years old he made an apple-paring machine, with which at the " paring bees " held in the neighborhood he could accomplish more than a dozen girls. Soon after this achievement he began helping his brother in the manufacture of tacks. The operation consisted in stamping them out from a thin plate of iron, after which they were taken up, one at a time, with the thumb and finger and caught in a tool worked by the foot, while a blow given simultaneously with a hammer held in the right hand made a flat head of the large end of the tack projecting above the face of the vise. This was the only method then known, and it was so slow and irksome that young Blanchard often grew disgusted. As a daily task he was given a certain quantity of tacks to make, which number was ascertained by counting. Finding this much trouble, he constructed a counting-machine, consisting of a ratchet-wheel which moved one tooth every time the jaws of the heading tool or vise moved in the process of making a tack. From this achievement he passed to a tack machine, and after six years of hard work turned out an apparatus that made five hundred tacks a minute. He sold his patent for the trifle of $5,000.

With part of this money he began his experiments in turning musket-barrels, an operation that was simple enough except at the breech, where the flat and oval sides had to be ground down or chipped. Blanchard made a lathe that turned the whole barrel satisfactorily. While exhibiting his new lathe at the United States Armory at Springfield, occurred the incident that led to Blanchard's great device for turning irregular forms. One of the men employed in cutting musket-stocks remarked that Blanchard could never spoil his job, for he could not turn a gun-stock. The remark struck Blanchard, who replied, " I am not so sure of that, but will think of it a while." The result of six months' study was the lathe with which such articles as gunstocks, shoe-lasts, hat-blocks, tackle-blocks, axe-handles, wig-blocks, and a thousand other objects of irregular shape may now be turned. While at Washington getting his patent, Blanchard exhibited his machine at the War Office, where many heads of departments had assembled. Among the rest was a navy commissioner, who, after listening to Blanchard, remarked to the inventor: " Can you turn a seventy-four ? "

" Yes," was the reply, " if you will furnish the block." Blanchard afterward made many interesting experiments in steam-carriages, but his chief claim to fame rests upon his lathe.

RICHARD M. HOE AND THE WEB-PRESS.

From the end of the first half of this century date movements of extraordinary importance in the world of American invention. The locomotive, the steam-engine and steam-boat, the telegraph, reaping-machine, the printing-press, all seemed to reach an era of wide usefulness at about the same time. It was in 1814 that Walters first printed the London *Times* by steam, the sullen pressmen standing around waiting for a pretext to destroy the machinery, and only prevented by strategy from doing so. About thirty years afterward Richard M. Hoe first turned his attention to the improvement of printing-presses. The founder of the famous house of printing-press makers, Robert Hoe, was born in England. His son, Richard March Hoe, was born in New York on the 12th of September, 1812. He made his first press in 1840, when he turned out the machine known as " Hoe's Double-cylinder," which was capable of making about six thousand impressions an hour, and was the admiration of all the printers in the city. So long as the newspaper circulation knew no great increase this wonderful press was all-sufficient; but the greater the supply the greater grew the demand, and a printing-press capable of striking off papers with greater rapidity was felt to be an imperative need. It was often necessary to hold the forms back until nearly daylight for the purpose of getting the latest news, and the work of printing the paper had to be done in a very few hours. In 1842 Hoe began to experiment for the purpose of getting greater speed. There were many difficulties in the way, however, and at the end of four years of experimenting he was about ready to confess that the obstacles were insurmountable. One night in 1846, while still in this mood, he resumed his experiments ; the more he reviewed the problem, the more difficult it seemed. In despair he was about to give it up for the night, when there flashed across his brain a plan for securing the type on the surface of a cylinder. This was the solution of the problem, and within a year our leading newspapers had their " Lightning " presses, in which from four to ten cylinders were used to feed sheets of paper against the surface of the type as it flew around. So recently as 1870 the ten-cylinder Hoe press, printing twenty - five thousand sheets an hour, was considered a marvel.

Then came the perfecting press, a far smaller machine, but capable of five times as much work, thanks to the substitution of rolls of paper for separate sheets fed in one by one. The device by which the web of paper after being printed on one side is turned over and printed on the other side in the same machine was another triumph of American ingenuity. Stereotyping made it possible to print from a dozen presses at the same time without the trouble of setting up new type, and inventions for pasting, folding, and counting the papers still further increased the speed at which papers may be issued, while at the same time decreasing the number of men employed as pressmen. In 1865 it required the services of twenty-six men and boys to print and fold twenty-five thousand copies of an eight-page paper in an hour. To-day a perfecting press, with the aid of four men, does four times as much work. It has been recently estimated that to print, paste, and fold the Sunday edition of one of the great newspapers with the machinery of 1865 would require the services of five hundred persons.

THOMAS W. HARVEY AND SCREW-MAKING.

The gimlet-pointed screw patented in 1838 by Thomas W. Harvey, of Providence, R. I., is a marked instance of an improvement so useful that we can scarcely realize that less than fifty years ago such screws were unknown to the carpenter, for it was not until 1846 that Harvey succeeded in getting people to abandon the old blunt-ended screw that we now occasionally find in buildings put up before 1850. Harvey was a Vermont boy, born in 1795. His faculty for the invention of machinery for screw-making and other purposes gave him and his associates and successors —Angell, Sloan, and Whipple—great fortunes according to the estimate of that day. He died in 1856.

C. L. Sholes and the Typewriter.

A great many men contributed to make the typewriter what it is to-day—as much of an im-

C. L. Sholes.

provement upon the pen as the sewing-machine is upon the needle. So long ago as 1843 some patents were taken out for divers forms of writing-machines, all more or less impracticable. It was not until C. L. Sholes, then of Wisconsin, took up the problem, in 1866, that the present form of a number of type-bars, arranged so that their ends strike upon a common centre, was devised. Sholes died in 1890, having also helped by many minor devices the increase in the use of writing-machines. From 1865 to 1873 he made thirty different working models of writing-machines, devoting himself to the task almost day and night for eight years.

B. B. HOTCHKISS AND HIS GUNS.

American inventors have had, as a rule, but small success in making Europe see the value of their inventions before this country has proved it. Morse could get neither England nor France to take an interest in his telegraph schemes, and, at a later day, Bell's telephone was received in England as a curious device, but not worth investing money in. An exception to this rule may be found, however, in the case of B. B. Hotchkiss, a Connecticut inventor, who during the civil war conceived the idea of a breech-loading cannon. In 1869 Hotchkiss mounted one of his small guns in the Brooklyn Navy-yard, but found no encouragement to experiment further. The Franco-German war found him in Europe with a breech-loading gun that would throw shells. His success was such that there is not a civilized country where Hotchkiss guns, throwing light shells with a rapidity not dreamed of years ago, are not now in use. The inventor has made a large fortune and has had the pleasure of sending to this country a number of guns for our cruisers, the Atlanta, the Boston,

B. B. Hotchkiss.

the Chicago, and the Dolphin. So great is the rapidity, accuracy, and power of these Hotch-kiss rapid-fire guns that some experts expect to see two-thirds of an action fought with these or similar pieces, which they think will silence and put out of action all the heavy guns in a few minutes after the enemies come within fifteen hundred yards of each other. For instance, the latest piece is a six-pounder, which, with smoke-less powder, has a range of five thousand yards and an effective fighting range of one thousand yards, within which distance a target the size of a six-inch gun can be hit nearly every time and

five inches of wrought iron perforated. A speed
in firing of twenty-five shots a minute has been
attained.

CHARLES F. BRUSH AND THE DYNAMO.

A trifling incident revealed to an Italian savant the fact that when two metals and the
leg of a frog came into contact the muscles
of the leg contracted. The galvanic battery
resulted. Years later another observer discovered that if a wire carrying a current of electricity was wound around a piece of soft iron the
latter became a magnet. Out of these simple
discoveries have arisen the telegraph, the telephone, and a host of inventions depending upon
electricity. And to-day, with all the wonders
accomplished in this field, we are yet upon the
threshold of the enchanted palace that electricity
is about to open to us. Through its aid we shall
one day enjoy light, heat, and power almost as
freely as we now enjoy air. The crops will be
planted, watered, cultivated, gathered, and transported to the uttermost ends of the earth by
electricity. The steam-engine is said to do the
work of two hundred million men, and to have
been the chief agent in reducing the average
working hours of men in the civilized world in
this century from fourteen hours a day to ten.
But electricity, according to even conservative
judges, will accomplish infinitely more. It will
make possible the harnessing of vast forces of

19

nature, such as the falls of Niagara, because the electric current can be transported from place to place at small cost and it is easily transformed into light or power or heat. Within a few months we shall see the first results of the great work at Niagara. Before many years the power of the tides is certain to be used along the sea-

Charles F. Brush.

board for producing electricity. Here is a force equal to that of a million Niagaras going to waste.

The late Clerk Maxwell, when asked by a distinguished scientist what was the greatest scientific discovery of the last half-century, replied: "That the Gramme machine is reversible." In other words, that power will not only produce electricity, but that electricity will produce power. By turning a big wheel at Niagara we can produce an electric current that will turn another wheel for us fifty, or perhaps five hundred miles away. The dynamo is one of the great achievements of the day to which Charles F. Brush, of Cleveland, O., has devoted himself with much signal success. Brush was born in March, 1849, in Euclid Township near Cleveland, and his early years were spent on his father's farm. When fourteen years old he went to the public school at Collamer, and later to the Cleveland High-school, and as early as 1862 distinguished himself by making magnetic machines and batteries for the high-school. During his senior year in the high-school, the chemical and physical apparatus of the laboratory of the school was placed under his charge. In this year he constructed an electric motor having its field magnets as well as its armature excited by the electric current. He also constructed a microscope and a telescope, making all the parts himself, down to the grinding of the lenses. He devised an apparatus for turning on the gas in the street-lamps of Cleveland, lighting it and turning it off again. When he was eighteen years of age he entered Michigan University at Ann Arbor, and, following his particular bent, was graduated as a mining engineer in 1869, one year ahead of his class. Returning to Cleveland he began work as an analytical chemist and soon became interested in the iron business. In 1875 Brush's attention was first called to electricity by George W. Stockly, who suggested that there was an immense field ready for a cheaper and more easily managed dynamo than the Gramme or Siemens, the best types then known. Stockly, who was interested in the Telegraph Supply Company, of Cleveland, agreed to undertake the manufacture of such a machine if one was devised. In two months Brush made a dynamo so perfect in every way that it was running until it was taken to the World's Fair in 1893. Having made a good dynamo, the next step was a better lamp than those in use. Six months of experimenting resulted in the Brush arc light. Stockly was so well satisfied with the commercial value of these inventions that the Telegraph Supply Company, a small concern then employing about twenty-five men, was reorganized in 1879, as the Brush Electric Company. In 1880 the Brush Company put its first lights into New York City, and it has since extended the system until there is scarcely a town in the country where the light may not be found. Besides dynamos and lamps, the immense establishment at Cleveland employs its twelve hundred men in making carbons, storage-batteries, and electro-plating apparatus. Mr. Brush is a self-taught mechanic, able to do any work of his shops in a manner equal to that of an expert. He is intensely practical, never over-sanguine, and an excellent business man. If a delicate piece of work is to be done for the first time, he will probably do it with his own hands. He is not fond of experiment for the experiment's sake; he wants to see the practical utility of the aim in view before devoting time to its attainment. Of the scores of patents he has taken out, two-thirds are said to pay him a revenue. In 1881, at the Paris Electrical Exposition, Brush received the ribbon of the Legion of Honor. In personal appearance there is nothing of the round-shouldered, impecunious, studious inventor about him. He is six feet or more in height, and so fine a specimen of manhood that Gambetta, the French statesman, once remarked that the man impressed him quite as much as the inventor.

EICKEMEYER AND HIS MOTOR.

In the same field of electricity, as applied to every-day life, a Bavarian by birth, but an American by adoption, Rudolf Eickemeyer, of Yonkers, has done some valuable work in devising a useful form of dynamo. His machines are now used almost exclusively for elevators and hoisting apparatus, one large firm of elevator builders having put in no less than six hundred Eickemeyer motors within the last four years. As electricity becomes more and more useful for small powers, such as lathes, pumps, and elevators, an effective and simple motor becomes of the utmost importance. Rudolf Eickemeyer was born in October, 1831, at Kaiserslautern, Bavaria, where his father was employed as a forester. He was educated at the Darmstadt Polytechnic Institute and at once showed a predilection for scientific work. When still a boy he joined the Revolutionists under Siegel, and after the upheaval of 1848 came here with Siegel, Carl Schurz, and George Osterheld, the latter afterward becoming his partner. The young man's first work here was as an engineer on the Erie Railroad line, then building. In 1854 he established himself in Yonkers in the business of repairing the tools used in the many hat-shops of that already flourishing city. The next twenty years of his life were devoted to inventions and improvements in every branch of hat-making. His shaving-machines, stretchers, blockers, press-

Rudolph Eickemeyer.

ers, ironers, and sewing-machines substituted mechanism for laborious and slow methods of hand work. At the beginning of the war Eicke-meyer was quick to see the opportunity for turning his factory to other uses, and vast quantities of revolvers were made there. When that industry declined, he took up the manufacture of mowing-machines, having invented a driving mechanism for such machines that met with wide favor. The introduction of the Bell telephone in Yonkers first turned Eickemeyer's attention to electricity, and for the last ten years he has devoted himself almost exclusively to the invention and manufacture of electric motors. His first successful invention in this field was a dynamo to furnish light for railroad trains. From this he was led to the invention of a dynamo capable of doing effective work at much lower speed than that usually employed, and this has proved to be his most valuable achievement. Some improvements in winding the armatures have also been accepted as valuable and adopted by other manufacturers. In connection with storage batteries Mr. Eickemeyer has also done a good deal of interesting work. But he is chiefly known to the electrical world as the inventor of a most useful dynamo for power purposes. For the last forty years he has been one of the men who have most aided in the growth of Yonkers, taking great interest in all questions pertaining to its government and school system. He was married in 1856 to Mary T. Tarbell, of Dover, Me., and his eldest son, Rudolf Eickemeyer, Jr., is associated with him in business.

George Westinghouse, Jr., and the Air-brake.

George Westinghouse, Jr., to whom is due the railroad air-brake, and who was also largely instrumental in revolutionizing Pittsburgh by the introduction of natural gas, was born at Cen-

George Westinghouse, Jr.

tral Bridge, in Schoharie County, N. Y., in 1846. His father was a builder and, later, superintendent of the Schenectady Agricultural Works, and it was in the shops of these works that the boy found his vocation. Before he was fifteen he had modelled and built a steam engine. The

war took him away from work in 1864, but when
that was over he returned to Schenectady and,
although yet in his teens, he began to attempt
improvements upon every device that presented
itself. Sometimes he was successful. Among
one of his first valuable achievements was a
steel railroad frog that resulted in a good deal
of money and some reputation. This was in
1868. While in Pittsburgh making his frogs,
which sold well, he one day came across a newspaper account of the successful use of compressed air in piercing the Mont Cenis tunnel.
His success in the field of railroad appliances
had led him to study the question of better
brakes, and the suggestion of compressed air
came to him as a revelation. To stop a train by
the old methods was a matter of much time and
a tremendous expenditure of muscular energy
by the brakeman, whose exertions were not always effective enough to prevent disaster. Westinghouse consulted one or two friends, who were
inclined to ridicule the idea that a rubber tube
strung along under the cars could do better
work than the men at the brakes. Fortunately,
he was able to make the experiment, and the air-
brake was speedily recognized as one of the important inventions of the century.

When petroleum was discovered in the fields
near Pittsburgh, some ten years ago, Mr. Westinghouse was greatly interested, and at once
suggested that perhaps oil might be found near
his own home in Washington County. He decided to test the matter, and planted a derrick

on his own grounds. The drill was started in December, 1883, and at a depth of 1,560 feet a vein was struck, not of oil, as was anticipated, but—what had not been counted upon as among the contingencies—of gas. Gas was not what Westinghouse was after or wanted, but there it was, and not wishing to let it run to waste, he began to consider what use could be made of it. Other people who had been boring for oil also struck gas, which, taking fire, shot up twenty or thirty feet. If such gas could be made to serve foundry purposes, here was a gigantic power going to waste. Within three years the business grew to be an immense one. The company organized by Mr. Westinghouse owned or controlled fifty-six thousand acres, upon which were one hundred wells and a distributing plant of four hundred miles of pipes. Notwithstanding the failure of some of the wells since then, natural gas is an extraordinary boon for which Pittsburgh has to thank Mr. Westinghouse. Of late years this inventor's energies have been turned toward electric machinery for lighting and power, especially as applied to railroad purposes, and a number of useful devices have resulted. Mr. Westinghouse is still in the prime of life and is activity personified. He makes his home in Pittsburgh, and is naturally looked upon as one of its leading spirits.

The field of electric invention is so vast and so actively worked that one cannot take up a newspaper without finding reference to some new achievement made possible by this wonderful agent, whose real powers were unsuspected fifty years ago. Aside from the direct value of these inventions in promoting the comfort and increasing the wealth of the country there is another factor to be considered having the most vital relation to the industries of the country and its powers of production. The large number of inventions made in these United States implies a high degree of intelligence and mental activity in the great body of the people. It indicates trained habits of observation and trained powers of applying knowledge which has been acquired. It shows an ability to turn to account the forces of Nature and train them to the service of man, such as has been possessed by the laborers of no other country. It suggests as pertinent the inquiry whether any other country is so well equipped for competition in production as our own ; whether in any other country the mechanic is so efficient and his labor, therefore, so cheap as in our own ; whether he does not exhibit the seeming paradox of receiving more for his labor than in any other country, and at the same time doing more for what he receives.

THE END.